THE VIRGIN
INTERNET TRAVEL GUIDE

GW00392236

THE VIRGIN
INTERNET TRAVEL GUIDE
VERSION 1.0

Davey Winder

First published in Great Britain in 2000 by
Virgin Publishing Ltd
Thames Wharf Studios
Rainville Road
London W6 9HA

Version 1.0 – January 2000

Designed and typeset by John and Orna Designs, London
Printed and bound by Mackays of Chatham plc

ISBN 0 7535 0441 3

//IT'S THE BIGGEST TRAVEL AGENCY IN THE WORLD

'I want to go somewhere different this year.'
'What's the weather like in Brazil?'
'I booked my holiday on the Internet and saved a fortune!'

The Internet is revolutionising the travel industry, yet most of us still trot down to high-street travel agents to book our holidays. But in the last few years, Internet access from home, public libraries, and many other places has boomed – and with it has come the opportunity for everybody, whether or not they have their own PC, to cut out the middleman and make their own travel bookings direct.

What's more, the Internet is no longer the preserve of the computer boffin. Computers are cheaper than ever, Internet access itself is now free of charge and the constantly improving software used to surf the web is now both easy to use and powerful.

This book isn't a guide to the Internet itself. That's the domain of our companion volume, **The Virgin Guide to the Internet**. However, with comprehensive listings of more than 1000 travel web-sites, it is a collection of signposts to the travel-related resources lurking in its sometimes-unfathomable depths. Use this guide to track down the best online tourist guides, the cheapest way to buy flights and holidays and those vital insider travel secrets – and save time and money as you go.

Of course, the Internet is forever expanding and changing. We can't pretend to have covered everything, but we have trawled the Internet for the most useful, well-designed and well-maintained websites. The addresses listed here should provide a good service and be regularly updated by their operators.

Let this Virgin Guide be your springboard into the
world of Internet travel.

Davey Winder, who compiled this guide, is a founding member
of the Internet Society of England and a former Technology
Journalist of the Year. As well as being the author of more than
a dozen books about the Internet, he is Contributing Editor of
PC Pro magazine. Davey is happy to receive your emails at
davey@happygeek.com – but can't guarantee a reply!

//CONTENTS

1//THE INTERNET EXPLAINED

Now that the Internet has become part of our lives, everyone seems to have a different explanation for what it is. Some will tell you it is a vast library of information. Others will say it is something to do with the 'new media', a combination of all the most useful aspects of television and publishing. Yet others will say that it's a tool for global communication. They are all correct – yet none have answered the real question: what is the Internet? The Internet is actually a system of networks comprising millions of computers all over the world. Hook your PC, via your telephone and an Internet Service Provider (ISP), into this network and you will have access to all the others.

That's a pretty bare technical explanation, but the people that use it, and the things they use it for, also define the Internet. So a more meaningful explanation of the Internet would say that it is simply an effective global medium for communicating and exchanging information. Yes, the Internet is email and the World Wide Web and lots of other technologies, but above all it is the community of people who contribute to it and draw information from it.

By offering new ways to do things and making information, which was previously guarded by the few, available to all, the Internet has destroyed many hitherto accepted wisdoms. For travellers, it puts control over planning and booking in the hands of the users, giving them access to the same professional resources that have been the sole domain of the travel agent in the past.

All aspects of the Internet combine to provide these services: the World Wide Web is the window on to all the travel services that let you browse timetables, buy tickets, reserve hotel rooms, research destinations and more; email is used to confirm bookings and answer queries quickly; Usenet – the Internet's big public noticeboard – brings you into contact with other travellers who aren't afraid to tell you the truth about a destination or service, or who can make those all-important personal recommendations.

A very brief history of the Internet

In order to understand the Internet of today, it's useful to look back to its origins in the murky world of military research during the Cold War of the 1960s. The Internet was conceived towards the end of the decade, when the Advanced Research Projects Agency (ARPA), part of the US Defence Department, needed to establish a method of exchanging military research information between computers in different places. Existing networks operated on a circuit-switching basis, where the information was carried between the various computers in strict sequence: if one computer went down, so did the rest of the network.

For a more detailed explanation of the Internet, its history and its workings, why not read **The Virgin Guide to the Internet**?

Because of the sensitive information being carried on this military network, the ARPA scientists designed a system that would work even if a big chunk of it were destroyed by enemy action such as a nuclear strike. They helped to develop a method called packet switching, which broke information down into small bursts or packets of data, each of which was separately addressed and could take the quickest route at any given time to reach their destination – at which point they would all be pieced back together in the right order. Blow up a computer on a packet-switched network and the information being transferred simply takes a different route.

The first packet-switched network, ARPANET, was established in 1969, connecting just four sites across the US. By 1972 the figure grew to 40 sites, mainly universities, and electronic mail was being exchanged between non-military personnel. The network continued growing until, in 1983, there were so many institutions connected that the US military information exchange was moved elsewhere to preserve security.

The next big step forward came in 1989 when Tim Berners-Lee, a British physicist working in Geneva, wrote a program called World Wide Web. Initially this was to make physics research data easily available to anyone who needed it, using the concept of 'hyperlinks' to connect different collections of information. The idea was that you could be reading one document and if there were any hyperlinks in the text, which are displayed as highlighted words, you could use a mouse click to open up another document that delved further into the subject matter. These same links are the threads that connect information on today's websites.

The related documents don't need to be on the same hard disk, the same computer or even the same network. They can be stored on any computer, known as a server because it serves up the information, when requested, over a network. From the user's point of view, the storage location is irrelevant; all that matters is that when you click on a link, the information you want appears on your screen relatively quickly.

In 1991 Berners-Lee's ideas were announced to the world at large, and thrown open to anyone who wanted to develop them further. In 1994 the first web browser, called Mosaic, appeared. This turned the complex, text-based commands used to power the Internet into simple, graphical forms – in much the same way as the Windows operating system interprets incomprehensible DOS computer code into easy-to-understand icons and messages. Suddenly the mainly academic dominated network was open to home PC users, and numbers connected to the Internet soared. Current estimates put the number of regular Internet users at around the 100 million mark – and that figure is still growing fast.

Who's in charge?

The usual answer to this question is 'nobody', but this isn't the whole truth. There is no one body (academic, governmental or corporate) that has control over the whole Internet, but there are many influential organisations. Microsoft and Netscape, which produce the software that most people use online, are very important. Other companies – the telecoms companies like BT and AT&T, which build the infrastructure that carries all the data, major Internet Service Providers like AOL and search engines like Excite – also have a lot of clout. But none have any more control than the others. The closest we get to a supervisory body is a bunch of scientists, computer geeks and long-time Internet users called the Internet Society, or ISOC for short (**http://www.isoc.org**). Along with a handful of other non-profit-making organisations, administered largely by enthusiastic volunteers, ISOC is responsible for overseeing the standards that drive the Internet forward, the architecture of the networks it comprises, and the administration required to keep it all going smoothly.

Getting connected

It is really very simple to get connected to the Internet, and getting simpler all the time. Stay at any business-class hotel and the chances are that your room will provide you with Internet access through the television. The advance of digital TV brings with it the promise of similar Internet access through a suitably equipped television. Mobile phones have basic web browsing and email functions built in, and soon there could be refrigerators and microwaves with display screens built into their doors, for Internet access in the kitchen.

For most people, however, getting access to the Internet means using a home or business PC, a modem (a box that turns computer digital signals into sound signals that the phone line can carry –

and vice versa) and a standard telephone socket. Most modern PCs have a modem built in, but if not, they can be bought very cheaply.

Modems are rated by the speed at which they can transfer information. The fastest are rated V90 or 56K (they mean the same thing) and can download information on to your PC at 56,000 bits (units of computer data) per second. Buying anything slower is a false economy, as you will wait forever for information to appear on your screen – and run up a huge phone bill.

What you need
You will need the following items in order to access the Internet at home:

- A PC capable of running Windows 95 or higher – preferably a Pentium II or better; or a PowerPC Macintosh with System 8 or higher;

- a modem, the fastest that you can afford (probably built in);

- an ordinary telephone line;

- an account with an Internet Service Provider (ISP);

- software – including a web browser, email program and Usenet newsreader – which is usually supplied by your ISP.

About Internet Service Providers
Internet Service Providers (ISPs) are the middlemen between the big commercial telecoms companies, which push data around the Internet, and the ordinary user. ISPs use telephone lines to connect your modem to their modems and thence to their computer network, which is linked by cable directly to the Internet backbone – the freeways and motorways of the network, compared with the narrow side street of your phone line.

Choosing the right ISP is obviously crucial to your enjoyment of the Internet. But making a decision can seem awfully hit and miss. Do you go for an ISP that promises professional service in return for £10 or £15 of your hard-earned cash every month, or for the biggest ISP in the UK, FreeServe, which costs nothing at all?

If you want to try the Internet out, then use a free service. If you find that later on your needs have outgrown what it can offer (maybe you want to set up a small business and need some professional advice) then you can always change to a subscription service at that point. In the meantime you get all the benefits of being online but at minimal cost.

You don't even have to own a PC to use the Internet. Local libraries, cyber cafés and business centres will let you browse for an affordable hourly fee.

Browsers

A web browser is the navigation software that enables you to exploit the web, and the Internet, to its full potential. Fire it up, connect to your ISP and the web is there waiting for you on your screen. The browser acts as a windscreen on to the web, and your mouse is the steering wheel that enables point-and-click navigation of the waiting information.

Two giant corporate players, Microsoft and Netscape, have captured 95% of the world's web browsers. Netscape has the 'Navigator' browser, while Microsoft has 'Internet Explorer' (sometimes referred to as IE). Both are big and feature-packed, and both are free.

At one point Netscape had a near total monopoly on the emerging browser market and Navigator remains a popular and powerful browser choice. Microsoft came to the party a little late, but soon started playing catch up. It didn't take long for Bill's boys to leverage their advantage and take Netscape on head to head. Internet Explorer was integrated into the Windows operating system, and it has been suggested that this gives Microsoft an unfair advantage. At the time of writing, a long-running legal action is under way in the US to determine if that is indeed the case.

Which browser you actually end up using has as much to do with the ISP you use as your personal choice. They will supply you with a CD-ROM containing a browser when you join up with them, and most people will be happy to use whatever they're given. Some people think that Internet Explorer has a slight edge over Navigator, but performance is so similar that there is little reason to change from one to the other – they both work equally well – and your ISP is more likely to provide technical support for a product it has supplied than for other software you have installed.

Web browsers do more than just browse the web. Both Netscape Navigator and Microsoft Internet Explorer should really be described as Internet software suites because they both come with email software, Usenet newsreaders and chat systems as part of the package.

Plugging into interactivity

Interactivity – the ability of the user to give feedback and control what he or she sees – is what makes the web special. Some interactive features require you to install additional software to back up the basic browser. These little add-on programs are called plug-ins, because they plug into your browser and enable it to do more. Internet travel websites in particular make very good use of these plug-ins. You can use your mouse to take a virtual reality tour of a hotel room, watch a video of a resort destination or walk through the cabin plan of a cruise ship.

Don't waste time downloading plug-ins until you need to. The latest generations of the Netscape and Microsoft browsers come complete with the most popular plug-ins already integrated into the software. If a website warns you it can't display a particular piece of information because you don't have the right plug-in installed, follow the links and download it on demand.

Java is perhaps the best-known and most widely used plug-in, and all modern browsers are 'Java enabled'. Java is actually the name of a programming language used to create small programs ('applets') that run inside your browser. The applet itself is downloaded from the website along with all the other items like graphics and text that make up the page. It is then stored on, and run by, your PC. Common examples of Java on the web include clocks and news tickers, animated logos and images that change shape or colour when you move the mouse cursor over them.

Shockwave is another popular plug-in. Website developers use it to create high-quality animations and professional-looking presentations, and many travel sites feature impressive Shockwave guides to services or destinations. Again, the latest versions of browser software have the necessary plug-in built in, but most websites that use Shockwave will have a link to the manufacturers, Macromedia (http://www.macromedia.com), where you can download a copy.

It works by downloading a multimedia file when you connect to a Shockwave-powered website. You don't have to wait for the complete file to download before seeing the presentation, though. This is because the software uses a technique called streaming, which starts the playback after a short delay. This delay allows the player to run the file while it is downloading the remainder; it sets up a buffer zone so it never has to wait for more information to download and so interrupt the playback.

RealPlayer works in much the same way as Shockwave, with the streaming of video and sound from a website. Once installed, whenever you visit a website with RealAudio or RealVideo content, the player will start automatically and play the file in the browser window.

Internet traffic jams, where it seems to take ages for a website to load into your browser window, are a fact of life online. Don't let this slow you down too much. While you are waiting for one site to load, open a new browser window (press Ctrl-N) and connect somewhere else. Don't open too many windows, though – more than four can strain your system and cause your PC to crash.

//BEYOND THE WEB

For the vast majority of users, the word 'Internet' means the World Wide Web. With its appealing interface, the web is certainly the most attractive and easy place to start using the Internet, but there's a lot more to this extraordinary network than that.

Internet Relay Chat (IRC) is an instant online communication system. Although your 'conversations' are typed rather than spoken you get used to this very quickly indeed and you are soon so immersed in the flow of conversation that the mechanics become beside the point. There are no geographical boundaries to limit your conversation, although the language barrier can be a problem. Neither are there limits on the number of people who can join in a conversation at any one time. It's commonplace to take part in an IRC conversation with people from the UK, US, Western Europe, Russia and the Far East – all at the same time. This global nature of the medium makes it the perfect place to chat about travel and foreign cultures.

Be warned, though, that IRC is more a social medium than a business one. Think of it along the lines of talking in the pub or at a party rather than in a travel agency. It isn't used by businesses, so you are far more likely to find yourself talking to a student than a company director.

To use IRC, you will need some appropriate software to handle everything from connecting to the IRC server right through to keeping track of the flow of conversation. Your ISP should be able to recommend something, or you may want to download an application yourself from one of the Uniform Resource Locators (URLs) in the address book at the end of this chapter.

Usenet – where the newsgroups can be found – is like a collection of noticeboards. Every message that you pin to a Usenet notice-board, or newsgroup, can be read by anyone else who passes by and looks at it. If someone wants to discuss what you've said then they simply pin a reply to it, and soon a conversation has begun. There are tens of thousands of separate newsgroups within the Usenet system. These cover every conceivable subject and, inevitably, that includes travel.

To take part in the discussions, you select a newsgroup using a piece of software called a 'newsreader'. This will probably already be on the CD supplied to you when you signed up with your ISP. The Netscape Messenger email program and Microsoft Outlook Express are both email systems and newsreaders.

Usenet does have its own rules of etiquette. Charging in like a bull in a china shop with disregard of these rules is asking for trouble. At best, people will ignore you; at worst, they will 'flame' you – the online equivalent of getting a good verbal roasting. Take the time to read the FAQ (Frequently Asked Questions) file posted in most newsgroups, and read back through a few days' worth of postings, and you will soon get to grips with what's OK and what's not OK within that particular Usenet community.

Usenet newsreaders Although there are many different varieties of newsreader software, they all operate in the same fashion. To start with, you need to configure the software so it knows where to go for your Usenet access. This is done in much the same way as your email software: both need to know the location of the relevant message server. Your ISP should have provided these details with your account and may well have pre-configured the software with these details. If not, check the technical support pages for your ISP on the web and look for the name of a news server, which will take the format news.your-isp.com. Enter this as the news server in the preferences or options section of your email software.

Subscribing to a Usenet newsgroup does not involve parting with cash, nor completing any forms. It is just another way of saying 'joining' and is as simple as clicking a button in your software to subscribe and another to unsubscribe if you get bored.

Once this is done, the news server name will appear in your list of folders, beneath the entries for inbox, outbox, sent items and deleted items. Click on this folder and the software will connect to the server in question. The first time you do this it will need to download the full list of Usenet newsgroups accessible through your ISP: be warned – as this list may carry details of more than 25,000 different groups, this process can take several minutes to complete. However, you only need to do this once, and when done you have a searchable list of newsgroups stored on your computer. When you select 'subscribe to newsgroups', it is this list that displays on screen. Rather than browse through them all, you can simply enter a keyword that describes your interest, such as travel, and hit the 'search' button. Now only those newsgroups that match your search will be displayed. Either double click the newsgroup name or select it and click on subscribe in order to be joined to that discussion group.

When you first subscribe to a newsgroup there may be anything from a few hundred to a few thousand available messages, depending on how busy the group is. The newsreader software will give you the option of either downloading all those messages or just a number of your choice. It is advisable to read back a little way so as to get an idea of how the group works, and how the conversation flows, so a figure of somewhere between 100 and 200 is recommended.

Because ISPs choose which newsgroups they carry on their news servers, you may find that a particular newsgroup you are interested in isn't available. If this is the case then the best course of action is to simply contact your ISP and request them to carry it. More often than not, they will oblige and the newsgroup will appear within a few days.

The software won't download the entire body of each message, but rather just the subject headers. You can browse through these and when you see a discussion that takes your interest just click on it and the newsreader connects to the news server and downloads the text of the message. Messages that form a conversation are grouped together by the software, so you can follow the discussion easily – this is called threading.

Joining in the discussion is simply a matter of hitting the reply button on the toolbar, which will pop up a text composition window similar to the ones used for email. Write your message, hit the send button and it is posted into the Usenet newsgroup for all to see. If you want your reply to be seen only by the writer of the message, rather than the whole newsgroup, then just select the 'reply to sender' button instead of the 'reply to group' button in your software. To test that your software is working, but without annoying hundreds of thousands of people by posting a message that just says 'sorry, testing', you should subscribe to the alt.test newsgroup and post away there.

Unless you spend a great deal of time in a vast number of Usenet newsgroups, you should find the newsreader software provided with Outlook Express or Netscape email perfectly adequate. If you do become a Usenet power-user then you can upgrade to a suitably powerful program such as Free Agent, which can be downloaded from **http://www.forteinc.com.**

It is even possible to access Usenet without a newsreader at all, by using just your web browser. Simply connect to a website called Deja (**http://www.deja.com**) and you can read and post messages in thousands of newsgroups from within your browser window. Ideal if you only want to dip your toes in the water occasionally and can't be bothered to set up your newsreader software for the task.

Guidelines for using newsgroups

When taking part in a Usenet discussion, follow these simple rules:

- Always read right to the end of a conversation before jumping in with a response. Someone else may have already said what you were going to say, so don't waste everyone's time – including your own.

- By all means quote the relevant sections of a message you are replying to, enough for it to make sense. But don't quote it in its entirety because that's another waste of everyone's time.

- Don't post adverts where they are not wanted, and don't post the same message to lots of newsgroups. These actions are seen as 'spamming', the online equivalent of junk mail, which is a cardinal sin on the Internet.

Mailing lists Pre-dating Usenet, mailing lists first saw the light of day as long ago as 1975 and are, essentially, communities of like-minded folk discussing a specific subject matter using the medium of email. Often thought of as the most civil of online discussion forums, mailing lists are certainly less chaotic than Usenet and more mature than IRC.

The mechanics of a mailing list are not rocket science, which is why there are more than 90,000 separate lists up and running as we go to print. The list itself is nothing more than a piece of software sitting on a mail server somewhere on the Internet. That some-where may be a dedicated machine at a big ISP or, just as likely, a PC in someone's back bedroom. This software, most commonly a program called LISTSERV (which explains why you might hear some people referring to mailing lists as listservs), performs two functions.

Keep the welcome message that is sent to you when you join a mailing list. This will tell you how to unsubscribe should you wish to leave the list. Remember that if you are going away on holiday then it's always a good idea to unsubscribe before you leave to save having an overflowing mailbox on your return.

First, it accepts email postings to a given list from any member who emails a message to it and, second, it distributes these postings to all the other members of that list. For the user, this means that a mailing list is no more complicated than reading and responding to email. You join a mailing list by sending a subscription message to the list address, which you can find from a list directory such as Liszt (http://www.liszt.com). This will either be automatically dealt with by the software, registering your name and so qualifying you to receive list postings, or it may be referred to whoever operates the list for approval. A moderator, as they are called, is usually the person who created the list in the first place.

The best mailing lists are the moderated ones, where someone first reads messages before passing them for distribution to the list members or editing/deleting them. This ensures focus on topic conversation and does away with the advertising, irrelevant and offensive messages that can appear on Usenet. There are un-moderated mailing lists, but here it is more a case of potluck as to whether they work or not.

Useful travel-related lists include 'bnb-list', for discussing bed and breakfast lodgings, 'ResourcesToGo', for disabled travellers and their companions, and 'green-travel', for the environmentally friendly holidaymaker.

You can always start your own mailing list if there isn't one that suits your particular travel interest. CoolList (**http://www.coollist.com**) lets you do this simply by filling in an online form. All the administration work is done from the website, and it really is as easy as it sounds.

//ELECTRONIC MAIL

The World Wide Web may be the face of the Internet, but its heart is undoubtedly email. A fast and convenient method of communication that is generally agreed to be the one thing above all else that drives people to want to use the Internet. The necessary programs, like Outlook Express or Netscape Messenger, are provided free by your ISP. These programs enable you to index and archive your messages into folders – they are a bit like word processors, with useful features including spell checkers. You can read your mail offline (after collection), send photos or sound clips as attachments and keep detailed address books of your contacts.

An alternative is to use a web-based service such as HotMail that uses your web browser to send, receive and compose mail – and they enable travellers to get access to email no matter where they are. Just pop into a library or Internet café in a foreign land and your email is as easy to read as if you were sitting at home. Web-based email is free, flexible, reliable and highly recommended for the traveller.

Domain names addressed

Any Internet address – be it for a website, an email address or anything else – is made up of several segments. Take the purely fictional '**hippo@zoo.madeup.co.uk**' email address as an example. Like all email addresses, it is divided into two halves by the '**@**' symbol. Anything before the @ relates to the user – in this case a chap by the name of hippo – while everything after it relates to the network. So a message sent here would be dropped into a mailbox called hippo, which is located on a dedicated computer or server called 'zoo', which resides at the 'madeup. co.uk' domain. That domain is also divided further into sub-domains: 'madeup', which is an identifying name of an ISP, company or individual; a domain type, 'co', which in this case tells us we are dealing with a commercial company; and a top-level domain, 'uk', which denotes either the country of origin, as in this case, or the organisational type.

Domains are also used to create web addresses, also known as Uniform Resource Locators (URLs). So the Virgin Publishing website at the URL **http://www.virgin-books.com** has a domain of 'virgin-books.com'.

Each computer or website on a computer connected to the Internet has a machine-friendly address consisting of four sets of numbers, each less than 256, which acts like an online postal code in identifying its exact location. A domain name is the human-friendly version of this coded address, the two being mapped together by Internet-connected computers called Domain Name Servers.

There are many organisational codes that you will see as part of domain names on the Internet, which serve to identify the type of company, service or body that uses the domain in question rather than identifying a geographical location. The most commonly used include:

.ac   Academic institution

.co.uk Commercial concern in the UK

.com   A commercial concern

.edu   An educational institution

.gov   Government bodies

.mil   The military

.net   Network operations and Internet providers

.org   Miscellaneous non-profit organisations

Although organisational codes do serve to help identify a service type, they cannot be trusted 100%. This is certainly the case with '.com', which is used for everything from personal home pages to multinational corporations, and, as available domains become harder to find, it is increasingly a problem with the '.net' and '.org' codes as well.

Country codes Every country has its own suffix, which is very useful to the online traveller. An address that ends in '.jp', for example, tells us that the computer where the web documents are stored is located in Japan – so you can be reasonably confident that it speaks with some authority about that country, as opposed to, say, Finland. The following list decodes some of the most common country identifiers.

.ar	Argentina	.il	Israel
.at	Austria	.in	India
.au	Australia	.iq	Iraq
.bd	Bangladesh	.ir	Iran
.be	Belgium	.it	Italy
.br	Brazil	.jm	Jamaica
.ca	Canada	.jp	Japan
.ch	Switzerland	.ke	Kenya
.cn	China	.mx	Mexico
.co	Columbia	.nl	Netherlands
.de	Germany	.no	Norway
.dk	Denmark	.np	Nepal
.eg	Egypt	.nz	New Zealand
.es	Spain	.pe	Peru
.fi	Finland	.pk	Pakistan
.fr	France	.pl	Poland
.gr	Greece	.pt	Portugal
.hk	Hong Kong	.ru	Russian Federation
.id	Indonesia	.sa	Saudi Arabia
.ie	Ireland	.se	Sweden

.sg	Singapore	**.uk**	United Kingdom
.th	Thailand	**.za**	South Africa

You could be forgiven for thinking that the country code for the United States is .com, because you will hardly ever see a domain ending in .us. This anomaly exists because the US dominated the Internet before it expanded into to a truly global force, and so it wasn't thought necessary to identify themselves by a country code. Instead they used organisation codes such as .com, and by the time other countries were a significant online factor it was too late to change. It is true to say, therefore, that most US domains will end in .com but not all .com domains will be US based.

//MAKING THE MOST OF THE INTERNET

A combination of the popularity of the web and the ease with which anyone can publish pages on it has led to there being tens of millions of 'home pages' on the web. It has often been said that the web's greatest asset and biggest downfall is the fact that anyone can be a publisher. Unfortunately there is no guarantee that the pages you visit will be good ones, and the odds are stacked against you. For every useful, accurate and well-designed website online there are probably four total stinkers. Defining good or bad in a website context can only ever be subjective, but any site with no useful content, no workable navigation paths (and ultimately no point) is a dud.

Defining a 'good' website It's often said in newspapers, TV and other media that 'content is king'. This applies to the Internet, too. There is little point in the flashiest of site designs if ultimately the pages have no content of any use to anyone, but we can forgive a site any design lapses if the content is good enough. Websites that rely on flash effects – 'bells and whistles' in the trade – often don't have much else to recommend them. The best websites will offer a choice when you connect to the main page: one for a quick-loading, text-only version of the site, another for the full multimedia experience.

Good sites, then, have useful content presented in a quick-to-load and easy-to-navigate format. Bad sites don't. It doesn't take much experience to get to the point where you can quickly distinguish between the two and start skipping the latter within seconds of connecting.

Using bookmarks/favorites

The web is truly huge, with millions of websites totalling hundreds of millions of web pages and thousands of pages being added every day. When you find interesting websites, you'll want to go back to them. You could write the addresses down on a scrap of paper, but luckily your browser software can do all the hard work for you. You can simply save the URL of the site you're on within bookmarks (Netscape) or favorites (IE), and then return to it at any time.

Although the principle is very much the same, an address book for websites, the practice is very different between the two big browsers. Netscape stores the website addresses as a web page, that is, in HTML format, the coding language of the web. Internet Explorer stores them as individual shortcuts to the websites concerned, in much the same way as Windows creates shortcuts to files that can be saved on the desktop as icons. The advantage of the Netscape approach is that it makes it easy to copy your bookmarks and pass them to a friend, or switch between different browsers on different machines. The Internet Explorer approach makes it easy to drag and drop your favorites on to the desktop for a mouse-click quick launch straight to the site concerned. If you want the flexibility of the Netscape HTML formatting in Internet Explorer, you can use the 'export' option (in the 'File' menu) to create an HTML file containing all your favorites. All the shortcuts will then be converted to web page format.

Creating bookmarks and favorites in the first place really couldn't be easier. If you are using Netscape, just browse the web as usual, and when you find yourself at a website you want to bookmark, right click on your mouse and select 'add bookmark' from the pop-up menu that appears. The entry is then added at the end of your bookmarks list. You can add a bookmark straight into a folder of your choosing by clicking on the 'bookmarks' toolbar button and then selecting 'file bookmark' from the menu. This opens up a further menu showing all available bookmark folders from which you can select the most relevant.

If you are using Internet Explorer, you can also do a right click with your mouse and select 'add to favorites' from the pop-up menu. This brings up a dialogue box that lets you select a folder in which to store the bookmark, or create a new folder if a relevant one doesn't exist. You can also have a frame on the left-hand side of your browser window displaying the contents of your favorites folder by clicking on the 'favorites' toolbar button, the one that looks like a folder with a star on it. Not only does this show all the shortcuts and their folders on screen, but there is also an 'add' button that creates new ones.

One of the problems with bookmarks is that the names they are stored under can be confusing. This is because the browser just rips out the title that the website designer has given to that particular page. Which is fine if the title is relevant and meaningful, but all too often it isn't. You can rename this to anything you like so that you know exactly where that bookmark will take you. In Internet Explorer select 'organise favorites' from the Favorites menu, then select the entry in question from the directory window that appears. Click on the 'rename' button, type in a new name and that's done. Netscape users click on the 'bookmarks' button and select 'edit bookmarks' from the menu. Find the relevant entry in the directory window, right click over it and select 'bookmark properties' from the pop-up menu. Edit the name here and you are finished.

If you always go to the same bookmarked site when you first connect to the web, why not set up that site as your browser home page – the page your browser looks for as a first port of call? For Netscape users select 'preferences' from the 'Edit' menu and then click on 'Navigator' in the category window. In the middle of the preferences window is an entry for 'home page'. You can either type in a website address or if you are already connected to the website in question you can just click on the 'use current' button. Internet Explorer users should head for the 'Tools' menu and select 'Internet Options'. The very first entry box is the one you want, again marked 'home page'. Type in the URL, select the current page, the default (which is the Microsoft Network portal website) or use blank. The latter means that when you start IE it won't try and connect to any site, but will just display a blank page.

You can use these same 'organise' and 'edit' options to sort your shortcuts into meaningful folders. Just create a new folder using the menu options you will find here, and drag and drop the website entries into the relevant folders. Sorting entries into alphabetical order in Netscape is a time-consuming process of dragging items up and down the screen using your mouse until you are happy with the order. To get the same result in Internet Explorer is much easier. Simply click on the Windows 'Start' button and move up the menu to the 'Favorites' entry. Move the mouse cursor over to the menu of favorite items and right click anywhere here, select 'Sort by Name' from the pop-up menu and all the shortcuts in all the folders will instantly be sorted alphabetically.

//THE ONLINE TRAVEL INDUSTRY

This guide will point you in the right direction of all the best online travel resources. The Internet can provide you with all you need to know before you leave for that important business trip or holiday. It can help you get to the right destination, at the right price, with the minimum fuss and maximum flexibility. Think of it as a whole library of travel guides, all linked together and accessible from your PC. More and more travellers are starting their journeys online, from researching a destination through to buying the flight tickets and reserving the hotel room.

The Internet offers convenience and control that conventional travel agents just can't. The Internet brings the entire travel industry into your office or home – many of the sites are linked into the same dedicated bookings network used by travel agents – to be used at a time that suits you.

> The Internet is open 24 hours a day, 365 days a year. The author has made travel arrangements including booking flights, reserving hotel rooms and car rentals while wearing his pyjamas at 3 a.m.

Another important plus point for the online traveller is the sheer amount and quality of the information and facilities available. If you like to book your aircraft seat before you reach the airport check-in desk then the Internet can help. Many flight-booking websites have a 'seat selection' feature, or you could try The Trip (**http://www.thetrip.com**), which gives you a picture of the seats available on a flight and lets you click on the one you'd like to reserve. Book a hotel room on the Internet and more often than not you will be able to choose from a full and precise listing of room types, complete with such essential details as the size of the bed and what's in the mini-bar. What's more, websites such as Expedia (**http://www.expedia.com**) show all the different tariffs.

These can make extremely interesting reading, as the costs for exactly the same room, but offered on different pricing plans, can vary by as much as 50%.

Online travel is taking off

According to a survey commissioned by ABTA, the Association of British Travel Agents, 45% of Britons would be prepared to book travel online if they knew how to go about it. In the US over a third of all Internet connected households researched travel online during 1998 and 20% actually made an online travel booking. In 1998, online travel sales in the US were a staggering £1.8 billion, a figure that looks certain to top £5 billion in 1999. The 'no frills' airline operators are predicting that within 3 years 30% of their sales will be made online, and UK airline Easyjet has claimed a world record 13,000 online bookings in one day.

Your first portal of call

The larger ISPs, and many of the big search engines, provide 'portals' – pages designed to act as a gateway or starting point to the rest of the web. From here you can go straight to a weather report, news headlines, financial information or entertainment pages. Most portals let you customise the layout of the page you see when you connect, deleting items of no interest and adding others that are. Many of them have specialised travel channels that are well worth a look, and can be good starting points.

The travel industry has also embraced the portal business model, and there are specialist portals that let you search for flight schedules and fares, hotel rooms, weather reports, destination guides and the like from a central portal page. Most of these all-in-one services also feature online booking systems so when you find what you are looking for you can buy it there and then.

Good examples of the travel portal include Microsoft's Expedia (**http://www.expedia.com**), My Travel Guide (**http://www.mytravelguide.com**) and The Trip (**http://www.thetrip.com**).

See where you're going

Webcams are inexpensive video cameras used to send live images across the Internet. One common use is for video conferencing, enabling you to see the person you are speaking to on the other side of the planet while only paying for a local phone call to connect to your ISP. For travellers, however, they offer a different treat, enabling them to see live video images of the beach outside a hotel, the weather abroad, or a bustling market square. For a comprehensive list of webcams on the Internet that are looking out on locations around the world try The World Right Now (**http://www.cam-orl.co.uk/world.html**). There's also a selective list of webcams at the end of this chapter.

If you're travelling on one of the major scheduled airlines, leave your ticket purchase to the last minute for some remarkable discounts. Generally speaking, the best fares can be found on a Wednesday for flying the following weekend. Hotel rooms, however, should always be booked as far in advance as possible – online or off.

Security

There was a time when people were scared stiff of buying anything over the Internet using their credit card, for fear that the details would be intercepted by a hacker and used fraudulently. Now, as electronic commerce (e-commerce) and the Internet have matured, everything has changed. In fact, a secure Internet connection offers far and away the safest method of paying by credit card – it's much more secure than giving your number to a complete stranger over the phone or handing a card over to a waiter in a restaurant.

The industry now uses a technology called Secure Sockets Layer (SSL) to run secure servers – computers used just for dealing with payments and orders. These specialised machines encrypt, or scramble, credit card details using military-strength codes.

Digital certificates also play an important part in online security, acting in much the same way as a passport or driving license in the real world. These digital IDs provide the necessary means of identification so that your computer knows that it is talking to a particular service, rather than some website that happens to claim to be that service. They also play a vital role in the SSL process. When you connect to that remote secure server, your browser asks to see the digital certificate of that site in order to establish its identity. Only when a valid and current certificate has been presented will the secure connection be made.

For every website that can't be bothered to implement proper secure servers to handle your financial transactions with them there are 99 that can. This means there are 99 better places for you to take your business.

Do not make a credit card payment online unless you are sure that it is being made over a secure server. Look for a locked padlock symbol at the bottom of your web browser. If you see an open padlock then the connection is not secure and should not be trusted. Similarly, if a window appears warning you that a digital certificate has not been recognised, follow the instructions you will be given to find out more information about the reasons why. Unless you are 100% happy with the site you are about to do business with, the advice is simple – don't do business with it.

There is another important question here: how can you tell you are dealing with a respectable company? The well-known companies such as high-street travel agents or international airlines should give you no cause for concern. But the really interesting, innovative companies are usually less than two years old – and many are hardly household names. Here you have to rely on your common sense. If there is a telephone number shown for the company, call it and make sure it is answered in a professional manner and not by a spotty oink in his back bedroom. Check that there are full details of the company, including a terrestrial address, email and fax numbers.

If the agent is bonded by an organisation such as ABTA (the Association of British Travel Agents) you can get your money back if the firm goes bust. Similarly, companies selling air travel in the UK, for example, are required to hold an Air Travel Organiser's Licence (ATOL). These also protect the consumer not only from losing money, but also from being stranded abroad should a travel firm go bust.

European Union rules also offer protection to consumers in member countries and state that any seller of pre-arranged package holidays must provide insolvency guarantees, bonding or insurance, regardless of that operator's size. The rules apply equally to Internet travel agents as they do to high-street agents. The main stipulation is that the rules cover you if your package is sold at an all-inclusive price, is for more than 24-hours' duration and includes any two of accommodation, transport or other tourist service that forms a significant part of the package.

Of course, if you are truly paranoid then most travel sites will give you the option of telephoning a real live human being to complete your purchase of flights or holidays.

Also watch out for websites that have been okayed by consumer groups such as the UK Consumer Association's 'Which Web Trader' scheme, or the global TRUSTe initiative. Both are working towards making it easy to spot 'safe' online shops by using logo schemes backed up by strictly enforced contracts covering consumer rights and fair trading policies.

You can also do a lot to protect yourself from administrative errors and simple mistakes that are always going to occur whether you book online or off. You wouldn't dream of chucking your travel documents, confirmations and invoices in the nearest litter bin after leaving the travel agent's. But people are not always so careful when it comes to electronic paper trails. Keep all copies of your electronic correspondence, and that means printing out the website's booking confirmation screen (just hit the printer icon on your browser) and any email confirmations you receive. If you are asked to note down a booking reference then do so, or customer services find it difficult to help you with any queries.

//NOW READ ON

In the following chapter you will discover the secrets of searching the Internet for the precise information you need and how to filter out the rubbish that you don't. Next we will introduce you to the traveller's best friend, the Internet community that will provide you with down-to-earth advice and hard-to-find detail on everything from the weather in Singapore and the best way to pack for a round-the-world trip to those places experiencing political or civil turmoil that are best avoided.

Chapter 4 lives up to the Internet's promise of shrinking the world by bringing local information on destinations around the globe right into your web browser. Official tourist board and government sponsored websites mingle with personal home pages to provide a balanced view of the planet.

If you want more than just sun, sand and sangria then you'll be well served by our chapter on activity holidays. From canal boats to African safaris, mountain climbing to mountain biking, it's all on the Internet and a cross-section of the best sites have found their way on to these pages.

Chapter 6 gets to the real meat and potatoes of Internet travel – how to get there and where to stay. Trains, planes and automobiles are covered in addition to every conceivable type of accommodation including a bizarre bed and breakfast establishment using jacuzzi-equipped railway carriages.

The seventh chapter, however, will appeal to those for whom money is no object. We tackle finding first-class services using the Internet and track down the ultimate in travel experiences including a flight to the edges of outer space in a MiG jet fighter, plus a trip into outer space on the world's first consumer space ship. More traditional luxury holidays such as world cruises and opulent trains are detailed as well.

Chapter 8 brings together all the experience of the seasoned traveller online to create an Internet insider's guide to getting the best from your travel experience. We cover everything from keeping in touch while away and sending electronic postcards to using your notebook computer on your travels.

Our FAQ section answers the most commonly asked travel and technological questions. And, of course, there's a glossary to explain the inevitable jargon of the Internet world.

Finally, every chapter in the book has an address book, with lots of URLs to help you on your way. And this chapter is no exception.

//ADDRESS BOOK

INTERNET REFERENCE

Modem Help   http://www.modemhelp.com
If you've got any problems with your modem, no matter the make or model, then the modem help website is a pretty good place to get them sorted.

NetBenefit   http://www.netbenefit.co.uk
All you could possibly need to know about Internet domain names packed into the one website along with the facility to register a domain name of your own.

Newbie University   http://www.newbie-u.com
If you are new to the Net, a 'newbie' in slang terms, then head over for the Newbie University and take a free course in the web, email, Usenet and other Internet applications.

The Internet Society   http://www.isoc.org
The nearest thing the Internet has to a governing body. The website is packed with information ranging from Internet history to standards.

INTERNET RESOURCES

Browsers

Browser Watch   http://www.browserwatch.com
A website devoted to browsers and featuring all the latest news about both Microsoft and Netscape. Plus lots of plug-ins and accessories to download for an easier online life.

Microsoft Internet   http://www.
Explorer   microsoft.com/windows/ie
Features, upgrades, tips and technical support for the market-leading web browser. A typically impressive website from Microsoft.

Netscape Navigator   http://home.netscape.com

Just follow the 'browsers' link to find pages packed with tools, plug-ins and the latest upgrades for Netscape Navigator.

Opera   http://www.opera.com

A small and speedy alternative to the big two browsers. Not so feature-packed, not free, but small enough to fit happily on a not-too-powerful notebook PC.

Internet Relay Chat

IRC Help   http://www.irchelp.org

More than 800 files relating to IRC, including FAQs, primers, beginners' guides and downloadable software.

MIRC   http://www.mirc.co.uk

Probably the most widely used of the IRC software packages, and a quick glimpse around the website reveals why. Powerful and friendly, website and software alike.

PIRCH   http://www.pirchat.com

Another IRC program that is gathering support amongst Windows 98 users. No, we don't know what PIRCH stands for either.

Snak   http://www.snak.com

An IRC software client for Macintosh users. The website includes full feature lists and hardware requirements, and offers online technical support.

Mailing Lists

Coollist   http://www.coollist.com

A free web-based service that lets you create and manage your own mailing list. No prior knowledge required, just the enthusiasm for the subject you want to cover.

eGroups http://www.egroups.com

A web directory of mailing lists sorted by category. Drill down until you find a list to suit or cut through to the chase with the speedy search engine.

Liszt http://www.liszt.com

The mother of all mailing list directories. Over 90,000 lists and a powerful search engine to find the ones you want. When you've found a list, subscribing is just a mouse click or two away.

PAML http://www.neosoft.com/internet/paml

The Publicly Accessible Mailing Lists' directory is small, only 7,500 entries, but is kept bang up to date and is well filtered to quality over quantity. Our example search for travel lists produced 50 interesting-looking lists.

Plug-ins

Acrobat http://www.adobe.com/acrobat

Another popular plug-in, and one that enables web designers to bring magazine-style formatted documents to their pages. All the details and the free viewer are here.

FreewareJava http://www.freewarejava.com

The perfect starting point for anyone wanting to know more about Java. Tutorials, FAQs and more than 600 Java applets nestle side by side here.

Macromedia http://www.macromedia.com

The company behind both Flash and Shockwave, two of the most popular multimedia plug-ins on the web. Download the free players here, and access some impressive demos at the same time.

QuickTime http://www.quicktime.apple.com

The amazing plug-in movie player that lets you view those 360-degree panoramic virtual reality presentations on the web.

RealPlayer　　　　　　　　　　**http://www.real.com**
All of the streaming media products from Real are available for download here. Choose between the fully functioning free versions, or the feature-heavy commercial products.

Usenet

CyberFiber　　　　　　　　　**http://www.cyberfiber.com**
A directory-style guide to Usenet, featuring an impressive transportation and travel section.

Deja　　　　　　　　　　　　**http://www.deja.com**
A huge searchable database of Usenet newsgroups. You can catch up on postings long-since deleted at your ISP, or simply use it to search across the board for specific travel-related keywords.

Free Agent　　　　　　　**http://www.forteinc.com/agent**
One of the most popular free Usenet newsreader programs. Powerful features make it ideal for the more advanced user.

Usenet Info Center　　　　　　**http://metalab.unc.**
Launch Pad　　　　　　　　　　**edu/usenet-i**
A useful introduction to Usenet, with history, FAQs and a news-group search engine for good measure.

Web-Based Email

Bigfoot　　　　　　　　　　**http://www.bigfoot.com**
A huge searchable directory of email addresses combined with a free web-based email service. If you don't mind being known as someone@bigfoot, that is.

HotMail　　　　　　　　　　**http://www.hotmail.com**
The service that started the whole free web-based email revolution remains the market leader – with a little help from Microsoft, which bought the company.

iName   http://www.iname.com

Free email with a twist, you get to choose from hundreds of different domain names for your address. How about someone@engineer.com or Europe.com for example?

Talk21   http://www.talk21.com

Highly publicised web-based free email service from British Telecom. As with all these services, setting up an account is just a matter of filling in a form on the website.

Yahoo! Mail   http://mail.yahoo.com

The latest in a long line of value-added services from Yahoo! The email system lets you get instant notification of new messages while you are browsing the web, by using the Yahoo! Messenger software. More details at the website.

CONSUMER RIGHTS

ABTA   http://www.abta.com

The Association of British Travel Agents' website is little more than an advert for its services and a directory for its members. However, there is some useful contact information should you need their services.

ATOL   http://www.atol.org.uk

An excellent guide to consumer protection when booking flights from companies in the UK, direct from the horse's mouth.

Consumer Gateway   http://www.consumer.gov.uk

A service operated by the UK Department of Trade and Industry offering advice on consumer matters across many markets, including travel.

Consumers in Europe Group   http://www.ceg.co.uk

Head for the 'package travel' pages and you'll find a comprehensive guide to European consumers' rights when it comes to buying holidays, online or off.

TRUSTe   **http://www.truste.org**
A global initiative to make the Internet a safe place to shop. All the information about the TRUSTe watermarking project, and the safeguards behind it, are on this informative website.

Which? Web Trader   **http://www.which.net/webtrader**
The well-known UK consumer organisation has taken to the web with a scheme to ensure online shoppers get a fair deal from member companies.

Internet Security

Digital Signature Tutorial **http://www.abanet.org/scitech/ec/isc**
A detailed yet very readable tutorial covering digital signatures from the American Bar Association.

Verisign   **http://www.verisign.com**
The leading supplier of digital certificates on the Internet. Their website is full of FAQs, and also offers you the chance to buy a digital ID of your own.

The WWW Security FAQ   **http://www.w3.org/Security**
An incredibly comprehensive question-and-answer session covering all aspects of web security, presented by the organisation responsible for web standards and chaired by the man who invented the web itself.

AROUND THE WORLD IN 15 WEBCAMS

LiveCam Vienna   **http://www.rlbnoew.at/livecam0.htm**
Live images of what is happening right now in Vienna, whenever 'right now' happens to be.

Live in Rio　　　　　　　**http://marcelo-botelho.com/today.htm**
The first live webcam in Brazil.

Montreal Cam　　　　　　　**http://www.montrealcam.com**
Ten tourist sites in Montreal exposed live on the web.

Capital FM　　　　　　　　**http://www.capitalfm.com**
Follow the links for 'Square Eye' to get live video from London's
Leicester Square.

Finnra Border Traffic　　　**http://www.tieh.fi/evideon.htm**
Live video of the traffic flow between the Russian and Finnish
borders.

Ski France　　　　　**http://www.skifrance.fr/webcam-f.htm**
Not one but eight webcams with varying views of French ski
resorts.

Signal Station Webcam　　**http://www.vegesack.de/webcam**
A view of the river in Bremen, Germany.

Dublin Webcam　　　　　　　**http://www.nci.ie/ispy**
When electronic Irish eyes are smiling … live view from an office
window in Dublin.

Window on the Wall　　　　**http://www.thewall.org**
The Western Wall in Jerusalem; a new video image every 60
seconds.

Cupola Live　　　　　**http://www.vps.it/propart/cupola.htm**
Looking out from the roof of a cathedral in Florence.

RealTime Tokyo　　　**http://www.nttls.co.jp/tower/tower.html**
The hustle of Japan's capital as seen from atop a tower block.

Web Cam Mallorca　　**http://www.geocities.com/~wcamallorca**
A Spanish webcam view and weather update in one.

Are Webcam http://www.arewebcam.com
Live from the hills of Sweden.

Ko Samui Beach http://www.sawadee.com/cam
Thailand's glorious beach.

Long Island New York http://www.lipreferred.com/bayview
Stunning views of the Great South Bay from West Bellport, New York.

Travel-Related Newsgroups

---

alt.travel
alt.travel.canada
alt.travel.eurail.youth-hostels
alt.travel.marketplace
alt.travel.ideas
alt.travel.road.trip
alt.travel.uk.air
alt.travel.uk.marketplace
rec.travel.africa
rec.travel.asia
rec.travel.australia
rec.travel.bed+breakfast
rec.travel.budget.backpack
rec.travel.caribbean
rec.travel.cruises
rec.travel.europe
rec.travel.latin-america
rec.travel.marketplace
rec.travel.misc
rec.travel.resorts.all-inclusive
rec.travel.usa-canada

2//SEARCHING

It has been said that finding the information you need from the millions of pages that form the World Wide Web is like finding the proverbial needle in a haystack. This is not the case at all. It would be far more accurate to compare the task to finding a pin in a whole field full of haystacks, while great hordes of farmers are building more haystacks as fast as they can. However, it is possible to make sense of the information stored out there; all it takes is a little knowledge of the tools available to help you and an understanding of how to use them.

The Internet really does contain all the travel information that you could possibly need to know. The trouble is, with a total of nearly one billion web pages to choose from, finding the ones that you are looking for requires just a little help. The way to find that needle in a haystack is to use specialised 'search sites' that attempt to categorise all the websites out there – and are consistently the most visited sites on the web. Connect to one of these sites, enter a keyword or two into a search box and press a button or hit 'return'. The search site then whirrs into action and returns a list – often a long one – of all the web pages it found that contained the words you were looking for.

Although most people tend to lump all search sites together under the generic term of 'search engine', this is in fact a confusing misnomer. Actually, there are three main types of search facility and knowing the right one to use for the search task at hand is vital.

The three basic search services are:

- directory sites;
- search engines;
- metasearch sites.

Directory sites

These are carefully compiled and catalogued links to websites, selected and checked for content by real people and arranged in directories and subdirectories that nest inside one another and house ever more specific types of content. Even though directory sites will have a search facility, when you use these sites you are actually searching just the directory itself (although some directories will refer the query to a search engine if they can't find a close match).

The selective nature of the directory helps to cut out much of the dross, and the accompanying reviews can also be a plus point, providing the service in question does a good job of writing them. The downside is that your searching is limited to the relatively small number of web pages that the site's cataloguers have actually inspected. Even the best known of the directory sites, Yahoo! (http://www.yahoo.com) is unlikely to have many more than 1.2 million links on its pages. Which sounds impressive enough until you compare it against the latest available estimates that say there are now approximately 800 million pages on the web as a whole. Another disadvantage is that directory sites often get out of date. It's hard for them to update the information they contain because they rely on human manpower to do the job.

However, this kind of search facility is the ideal introduction to finding stuff online. The best way to use it is to treat the selected sites as starting points for more detailed exploration, and it can be very rewarding to drill down into a category and browse the sites found there. Most directory sites are very user-friendly and intuitive, and they'll suit the newcomer to the web.

Search engines

These search sites depend largely on the information supplied by publishers of the web pages themselves. As we saw in the last chapter, every web page, no matter how complex, is held together by a programming glue called HTML (HyperText Markup Language) which controls all the words and pictures on the page and tells your web browser how they should be displayed. The HTML code also includes lots of information, such as site titles, page titles and content descriptions, which helps the search engine index the page correctly. HTML programmers can even use special sets of commands, known as 'meta tags', which specify the keywords that should be used to index the site. Most of the big search sites employ software processes called spiders, crawlers or bots to explore the web, looking for new pages to add to their indices; it is the meta tag information that these spiders collect and bring back to the database that the user can then search.

> The AltaVista search spiders visit an amazing 10 million pages every single day and, at the time of writing, AltaVista has a database of some 150 million web pages. But it still isn't the biggest search index online. That honour goes to Northern Light with an astonishing 175 million pages indexed.

The precise way that these software agents work varies from site to site. However, in general most of them either investigate a website in response to a request from that site to be added to the search engine index, or spend their entire life crawling around the millions of websites out there looking for new pages to add to the database. From the user's point of view, all that matters is that you can go to a search site, enter a keyword and get back a list of appropriate websites to visit. It is this database of detailed site information that is queried whenever you use a genuine search engine site. The software at the site uses a mathematical algorithm – a set of mathematical instructions – to determine a keyword relevancy ratio and return the best matches to the user, and all within the space of a few seconds.

When you use a search engine, you're looking at a much larger number of pages than a directory can access, and so you're more likely to find an exact match for your needs. But their power is also their problem. A search is likely to produce thousands of results for you to sift through. But there are several ways you can refine your search and limit the number of sites that are returned.

Metasearch sites

The latest additions to the web's information-mining armoury are metasearch sites. These work as a kind of Internet librarian or archivist, routing out your search requests to a number of other search sites and then collating the results that come back. In practice, this means that you make a single search request in the normal way by typing a keyword or two into box (just like a search engine) but this is then sent to several search sites simultaneously. The results that come back can be displayed in different ways according to the metasearch site you are using. Some display the results using a 'best relevance' or 'most recent update' indexing. Others group the results according to the search sites that produced them.

> When visiting any search site for the first time, go straight to the help section. This will provide you with all the information on how to get the best out of the service you are using and it will often include tips and tricks that can both speed up your searches and make them more accurate.

A good example of a metasearch site is the bizarrely named Dogpile (**http://www.dogpile.com**), which searches a dozen major search sites, four Usenet directory archives, newswires, stock quotes, weather forecasts, yellow pages directories and even online collections of maps.

//WHAT KIND OF SEARCH?

The key to searching with confidence in the increasingly crowded web is to select the appropriate site for any particular search. The method you use will depend on the amount of precision you need.

As a general rule of thumb, if you are looking for a website within a broad descriptive category, say a major airline or hotel chain, then the quickest option is to use a directory-based site such as Yahoo! – as you can be pretty sure that they have already categorised all airlines and hotel chains and have them waiting in neat indexes for you to browse. Rather than spend time drilling down to the right subdirectory, you can get there quicker by just typing a term into the search box and letting the directory itself present you with a link to the right directory section.

If, however, you have a more specific search to perform, say for hotels near Newark Airport, then you are better using the particular expertise of a true search engine such as AltaVista (http://www.altavista.com). Here you can enter the exact search required as 'Newark Airport Hotels' and get straight to what you're looking for.

Yahoo! passes queries it can't answer from its own directory to the AltaVista search engine. So this makes it a good all-round bet for most queries.

If your search is for something really very specific like, for example, the National Parks of Kenya, then a metasearch engine like MetaFind (http://www.metafind.com) will hunt the websites down from a whole set of search engines far quicker than you could hope to do if you went and checked them all yourself. Simply type 'National Parks of Kenya' into the query box and a long list of hits will be returned, sorted by keyword and, more often than not, plonking precisely the right websites at the very top of the list.

Most Internet searches would be a lot more successful if the enquiries were couched with more common sense. The first rule of successful searching is 'don't be vague'. The more precise your search request, the more chance the search engine stands of returning the right information for you. For example, a search for 'Brighton nudist beach' is likely to return more useful hits than if you had just searched for 'Brighton' and expected the search mechanism to read your mind about the nudist beach bit. However, search engines are becoming increasingly more subtle in the way they handle our requests. The ability to search for concepts and ideas instead of straightforward keywords is becoming a reality, thanks to advances in the complex mathematical calculations that are used to perform the search. These can often look for relationships between words and ideas, which makes it much easier to refine the search process.

Refining searches

The sheer number of websites returned by a simple search can be both overwhelming and disheartening. Do a simple search for New York at AltaVista and it will return with more than 4 million web pages that match the criteria. Assuming it takes three minutes to click on a link, wait for the site to load and have a look around, it would take more than fifteen years to visit them all.

In order to filter those matches down to a more practical number, it's necessary to refine the search. AltaVista, like many other search engines, has a handy refinement feature at the top of every search results page – a section headed 'Related Searches'. This consists of a list of related search phrases that the AltaVista software has produced in order to group sets of similar results together. Clicking on the more precise New York City suggested by the search engine will reduce the website results total to half a million or so. Another check on the 'related search' section reveals a new set of phrases including 'New York City Maps', which gets us the online map we were after, with a much more manageable (but still fairly astounding) 1,823 websites listed.

Some search sites, like Excite (**http://www.excite.com**), have a link beside their results that says 'more like this'. By clicking on this when you find a website that looks like it matches your requirements, the site will perform a new search based on the keywords it finds in the index for that particular page. More often than not, this will result in a set of websites that match your real needs better than the original search. Because it is using keywords from a site that is a close match, much of the hit-and-miss element caused by your uncertainty about the exact keywords to use will be eliminated.

If you are searching for a place name then capitalise it. If you do this, most of the search engines will realise you're looking for a place rather than anything else.

Every search site has its own strengths, weaknesses and characteristics. Take the Ask Jeeves site (**http://www.askjeeves. com**) which is designed to tackle questions in plain English. Instead of using search strings and keywords to form a query, Ask Jeeves wants you to pose a simple question. This conversational approach to searching is certainly intuitive as well as innovative. Instead of entering 'Paris flights' you would use 'Where can I buy a flight to Paris?' Most of the time the artificial intelligence techniques employed here work well, but it does regularly throw up some very bizarre results.

The fastest search For a turbocharged search, use the text only version of the AltaVista search engine. The search page loads in a flash, with no advertising and no graphics – just a search entry box and a button to click. Your searches are also speeded up because it takes less time to display them on screen. To turn on this mode, scroll right down to the very bottom of the AltaVista page. Here, in the small print, there's an option to 'set your preferences'. Click this to reach a configuration screen, tick the box marked 'text only view' and then hit the 'set preferences' button to complete the process.

Looking for pictures If what you are really after is a photograph of a particular destination or tourist attraction then some search sites have now implemented an image finder facility. Simply connect to one of these services and enter the place you want to see. Wait a few seconds and your screen will fill with small thumbnail photographs that match your search criteria. To visit the website that has the picture, and to see the full-size photo itself, simply click on the image and you are there. Some sites, like the AltaVista Media Finder, will, as the name suggests, also search for other media, like video or audio files. Try these sites to look for pictures:

- AltaVista Photo and Media Finder **http://image.altavista.com**

- Lycos Image Gallery **http://www.lycos.com/picturethis**

- Yahoo Image Surfer **http://ipix.yahoo.com**

Advanced searching
The key to sophisticated searching is, as Internet old hands and mathematical boffins alike know well, the 'Boolean operator'. This refers to a form of algebra invented by the English mathematician George Boole well over 100 years ago to analyse concepts by the use of simple defining words such as 'AND' or 'NOT'. Boolean logic is the prime method to define, and refine, web searches, because the Boolean operators speak the language of the database. The concept may sound daunting, but in practise it's easy. All you have to do is remember a few basic commands to tell the database

search software to either include or ignore a keyword from the search process. The key terms are:

AND or **+** Only looks for pages containing all the specified keywords.

NEAR Looks for documents where the specified keywords are within ten words of each other.

NOT or **-** Disregards pages that contain the specified keyword.

OR Looks for pages containing at least one of the specified keywords.

Groups together a set of Boolean commands to be used within a search string.

A search using the three words 'flights', 'schedule' and 'booking' will return a high number of hits because the search engine is digging out all the pages that contain any of those words. Using the operator '+' before each word – 'flights+schedule+booking' – signifies that the hunt should be only for pages containing all three words, and will reduce the results considerably. Add the word 'online', and the total reduces further; each time you add a word that has to appear in the page returned, you are reducing the number of results by focussing ever more tightly on your real requirements. You can use the '-' or 'NOT' operator to further specify the information you need. So, adding a '-US' to the search list – 'flights+schedule+booking+online-US' – should return a manageable set of websites where you can book European, Asian and African flights online.

And finally, you can create truly complex search queries by grouping together sets of Boolean instructions using brackets or parentheses. For example, if you wanted to search for pages that contained the word 'Caribbean' along with either 'Jamaica' or

'Bahamas', you could use 'Caribbean AND (Jamaica OR Bahamas)' as your search query string. This almost limitless flexibility in linking various concepts and thoughts by the use of algebra was not fully appreciated in George Boole's lifetime; it is only now, in the computer age, that his ideas have belatedly reached fruition.

Two simple search hints Quotation marks are another handy search helper, allowing you to search for a phrase rather than just a set of keywords. By enclosing your phrase in double quotation marks, the search engine is forced into looking for those keywords in that precise order, rather than located anywhere within the returned pages.

Wildcard searching – that's using the * symbol – can be particularly helpful when looking for foreign place names that you are unsure how to spell correctly. By replacing part of the word with the * symbol, you reduce the risk of a misspelling, which is guaranteed to fail. If you wanted to find some websites about Zimbabwe but didn't know how to spell it, entering the search keyword of Zimba* will get the same results as if you had entered the full name.

Ranking results

Most search engine software will try to put the websites that are most relevant to your enquiry towards the top of the list. As previously explained, they sort out the results of your search using algorithms, complicated sets of mathematical calculations, to determine the order in which the websites it extracts from the index should be displayed. In this process, known as relevance ranking, each document is graded according to how many of the specified search terms are contained within it, where the words appear in the document, and how close to each other they are. The perfect result is a document that has all the search terms close together towards the top of the page. Inevitably, some sites indulge in 'search spamming' and repeat certain keywords over and over again in order to try and fool the search engine. They tend to get noticed, and have their ranking reduced as a result.

Using browser search functions

Web browsers are getting increasingly helpful for searchers. The latest generations of both Microsoft Internet Explorer and Netscape Navigator feature built-in search resources. Simply connect to a website and then click on the 'what's related' button in the browser toolbar for a selection of links to similar sites to be displayed. Internet Explorer pops up the related site links in a search frame on screen, while Netscape uses a pop-up menu instead. Both work in the same manner, though: when you click on that 'what's related' button you are requesting your browser to perform a keyword search in the background. While you continue to browse the pages on screen, your web browser has made a note of the relevant meta tags and titles from the page you are looking at and sent these to a search engine dedicated to performing searches for either Microsoft or Netscape. It quickly scans its indices for any matches and the resulting hits are then sorted into order of relevance and sent back to your browser where they are formatted so as to appear in that search frame or pop-up window mentioned previously.

In fact, nowadays it is quite feasible to leave a lot of the searching donkey work up to your web browser software. The latest generation of Internet Explorer has a number of different search options available. The most obvious is the search button on the toolbar, which breaks out a search explorer bar in a frame on the left-hand side of your browser screen. To find a website on a particular subject, just tick the checkbox for the 'Find a web page' option, enter a keyword and off you go. The results of your search appear in the frame as live hyperlinks. Click on the most likely looking and the resulting website opens in the main browser window to the right, but the search results stay put on the left. This way you can easily navigate through a set of search results in double-quick time.

An explorer bar is just the Microsoft term used to describe the frame that appears on the left-hand side of your Internet Explorer browser. You can choose to display search information, a history listing of your online journeys, your favorites collection or even a directory view of your hard drive. Of course, you can also opt to close it completely if it takes up too much of your valuable screen space.

If you are using the British version of Internet Explorer 5, you may be disappointed with the very small choice of search engines in the explorer bar. However, you can cheat by adopting the more flexible US version. Simply go into the 'Tools' menu and then select 'Internet Options'. Hit the 'Languages' button on the first screen, click on the 'Add' button and select 'English (United States) (en-us)' from the list. Back in the main screen, highlight the (en-gb) entry and click on 'Remove'. Next time you start Internet Explorer you will get a much better choice of search engines. If you go to the 'Customize' option now, you'll notice a new button in the bottom left-hand corner marked 'Autosearch Settings'. This lets you specify a default search site, which you can use by typing any keyword, preceded by a + symbol, in the browser address bar – whereupon IE will automatically connect to the search site and display the results on screen.

Netscape users can make their searches a little more immediate by adding search buttons to the personal toolbar at the top of the browser window. Simply save the locations of whatever search services you want to use as a bookmark (see page 20), disconnect from the Internet, click on the bookmarks button and select 'Edit' from the options listed. In the Edit window you can easily drag and drop the search site bookmarks into the 'Personal Toolbar' folder. Now these shortcuts will appear as buttons on the toolbar, and each of the search engines is just a mouse click away.

Searching Usenet newsgroups

When it comes to travel news and views, make sure you don't miss out on the ongoing conversations that form the basis of the Usenet newsgroup discussion forums (see page 10). There are discussion groups that cover just about every travel topic and destination you can think of. Locating a relevant newsgroup is easy enough. Your newsreader software (usually supplied as part of your email or web browser package) will have the search tools built in. Just enter the keyword, for example 'Ireland', and the huge list of 20,000 or so newsgroups will be filtered down to just those containing the magic word.

Instead of trawling through thousands of websites thrown up by a search engine, why not ask the people who know? If you have a question about travelling around Britain in a caravan, simply join the newsgroup uk.rec.caravanning and post the question there. You might have to wait a while before someone replies, but for quality and personal recommendation, this route is unbeatable.

Finding a Newsgroup is one thing, but finding relevant conversations within the thousands of discussions taking place at any given time is another matter altogether. Luckily there are some specialist services on the web that can help. Perhaps the best known, and certainly the most useful of these, is called Deja (http://www.deja.com). You can use this like you would any search engine, entering a keyword or phrase to be searched for. But instead of searching websites, it confines its interest to newsgroups instead, returning a list of discussion threads for you to follow. You could also try a metasearch site like Dogpile, but make sure that you exclude all websites by ticking the 'Usenet' box. Both of these options can help you extract answers from deep within Usenet just as quickly as you can find pages on the web using a traditional search engine.

Guesswork Sometimes you don't have to use a search engine to search for sites. Educated guesses are some of the best-kept secrets for searching success. As you look at the listings in this guide you will notice that quite often the web addresses given are fairly obvious, consisting of little more than the place name with a preceding 'www' and a trailing '.com'. That's because everyone wants a web address that's easy to remember – and if you happen to be the official tourist board site for Bratislava then what could be more memorable than **www.bratislava.com**? It can be a good starting point just to hammer away at your browser with a few variations on the same theme.

If entering a .com address didn't work, find out the right country code in the table of top-level country domains on page 18. Take Berlin, for example: **www.berlin.com** just gets you a blank screen but **www.berlin.de** hits pay dirt. On a similar note, you can always try domain endings of .org and .net as well; in the case of Berlin, the latter also found an active website. However, be warned that playing 'hunt the website' like this can deliver some surprises. Many of these names have been registered by adult site operators with the aim of tricking as many people as possible into their website in order to ramp up the advertising revenue (the more visits the site gets, the more they can charge advertisers). The same operators also register misspellings of domain names so, if you're entering an address into the address bar by hand, be careful that you double-check the spelling before you hit the return key.

And finally

Even the biggest of the search sites can only hope to index about a fifth of the total number of websites actually out there. This statistical albatross around the neck of the search services can only get worse as the web grows at an exponential rate. Relying on any single search engine means that you are missing out on at least 80% of the sites out there. To cast as wide a searching net as possible, it's a good idea to make use of one of the metasearch engines.

One way of catching the numerous unlisted sites, and ensuring that the sites you visit are relevant to your requirements, is to check the links on any website you find to be useful. The chances are pretty high that they will have sites listed there that will interest you, as some will be on similar subject matters as the host site. Visit the most likely looking suspects and if you like them, bookmark them.

If the search site you are using has a button next to the search entry box marked 'advanced search' then click it. This will almost certainly open a new page with far more options for you to tick and search boxes for you to fill in. Generally speaking, the more information you can give a search engine, the better results it can give you.

//ADDRESS BOOK

Directory Sites

About.Com   **http://www.about.com**
Used to be called 'The Mining Co' but, despite the name change, it still specialises in having specialist directory areas hosted by named individuals.

G.O.D.   **http://www.god.co.uk**
Some interesting features make the Global Online Directory worth a second glance. These include the global search facility that lets you narrow your search by geographical location, right down to city level.

LookSmart   http://www.looksmart.com
For all intents and purposes a smaller version of Yahoo! but a lot easier to find your way around.

Magellan   http://www.magellan.com
One of the longer-established search directories. Provides star ratings along with the reviews.

Mirago   http://www.mirago.co.uk
Click on the travel and holidays button to go straight to the travel directory section, from where you can dig ever deeper into the directory structure until you find the precise information you require.

Northern Light   http://www.northernlight.com
A super-intelligent search site that groups results in folders of similar content. Unfortunately the more advanced search options cost money to use.

Snap Web Directory   http://www.snap.com
A vast-and-fast web directory site with a useful travel section that's well organised and easy to use.

Suite 101   http://www.suite101.com
A good travel section, aided by the fact that each of its subcategories are looked after by a volunteer editor to keep the content up to date and relevant.

UKPlus   http://www.ukplus.co.uk
A good, fast way to search for UK-specific sites. Plus the option to search the entire web is only a click away.

Yahoo!   http://www.yahoo.com
Everyone's favourite web directory site also happens to be the biggest and amongst the best. Hard to fault for either content or efficiency.

Specialist Travel Search Engines

Many search sites, in particular the directory-based ones, now have specific travel sections that bring together links to external websites with additional in-house editorial content.

About.Com Travel	http://about.com/travel
AltaVista TravelZone	http://search.thetrip.com
Ask Jeeves	http://www.askjeeves.com/channels/travel
HotBot Travel Directory	http://directory.hotbot.com/Recreation/Travel
InfoSeek Go Travel	http://infoseek.go.com/Center/Travel
Lycos UK Travel	http://www.lycos.co.uk/webguides/travel
Netscape Travel Channel	http://home.netscape.com/travel
SearchUK Travel	http://dir.searchuk.com/Travel
UKMax MaxTravel	http://www.ukmax.com/travel
UK Online Travel	http://www.ukonline.co.uk/content/travel.html
Virgin Net Travel	http://www.virgin.net/travel
WebCrawler Travel	http://www.webcrawler.com/travel
Yahoo! Travel	http://travel.yahoo.com

Search Engines

AltaVista
http://www.altavista.com

One of the biggest search sites on the Internet and also one of the fastest. As well as web page searches you can look specifically for images, video and sound. Plus a handy translation feature enables you to make sense of those foreign language websites you come across.

Euroseek
http://www.euroseek.net

A multilingual search engine that specialises in European content.

Go
http://infoseek.go.com

The home of the search engine that powers Yahoo! and many of the other big-name sites. As fast as you'd expect and accurate as well.

HotBot
http://www.hotbot.com

Wired magazine's search site is very US-oriented in design and approach. However, it is very fast and very efficient at turning up the right results.

Lycos
http://www.lycos.com

Lycos, one of the first search engines on the net, seems to be having difficulty in deciding if it is a search engine, directory or portal site. For the time being the search engine side of things seems to be winning.

WebCrawler
http://www.webcrawler.com

A slow response time and a clunky interface prevent this otherwise impressive search engine from being a serious threat to the opposition.

World Yahoo! sites

For finding local information, it makes a lot of sense to go to one of the independent Yahoo! sites operating from different countries. They specialise in material that is geographically and culturally relevant to their home country and will usually be presented in their native language. If you can understand the lingo, these sites will be your quickest and most accurate route to country-specific information and websites.

Asia	http://asia.yahoo.com
Australia and New Zealand	http://www.yahoo.com.au
Brazil	http://br.yahoo.com
Canada	http://ca.yahoo.com
China	http://chinese.yahoo.com
China (simplified Chinese)	http://gbchinese.yahoo.com
Denmark	http://www.yahoo.dk
France	http://www.yahoo.fr
Germany	http://www.yahoo.de
Hong Kong	http://hk.yahoo.com
Italy	http://www.yahoo.it
Japan	http://www.yahoo.co.jp
Korea	http://www.yahoo.co.kr
Norway	http://www.yahoo.no
Singapore	http://sg.yahoo.com
Spain	http://www.yahoo.es
Sweden	http://www.yahoo.se
Taiwan	http://tw.yahoo.com
UK and Ireland	http://www.yahoo.co.uk

Metasearch Sites

Debriefing   http://www.debriefing.com

The simple interface belies the power of this site. They're so confident of their efficiency that they display the speed at which your search was performed alongside the list of results.

Dogpile   http://www.dogpile.com

Perhaps our favourite of the metasearch sites. Mainly because it encompasses so many different search resources and isn't restricted just to the web.

Google   http://www.google.com

No frills, no fuss – just plain old-fashioned cutting-edge technology that somehow manages to filter out the rubbish better than most of the competition.

Highway 61   http://www.highway61.com

A complicated-looking interface makes this one for the more accomplished and confident searchers.

Metacrawler   http://www.go2.com

A slick front end that looks like a directory site. In use, however, the metasearch credentials shine through.

MetaFind   http://www.metafind.com

Flexible and fast, MetaFind is for the professional searcher in a hurry.

Specialist Sites for Travellers

Accommodation Search Engine   http://www.ase.net

It does exactly what it says on the packet. That is, it searches for accommodation in the country and location of your choosing.

Airlines of the Web   http://flyaow.com

A good place to come if you need to find if a particular airline has an online presence or not. If it has, it will be listed here and you can use the site search facility to locate it quickly.

Europe Today   http://europe-today.com/europe

In effect a search engine for European tourism. Information on maps, car hire, airfares, hotels, the Euro and even a best-filming-location finder for the movie industry.

Hotels and Travel Net   http://www.hotelstravel.com
Searchable links to more than 100,000 hotels and lodgings in 120 countries, plus guides, maps, airline info and travel chat.

Knowhere Guide   http://www.knowhere.co.uk
A user's guide to Britain. Type in a location and it will spit out information submitted by locals to let you know what it's really like.

World of Travel   http://www.worldoftravel.net
Dedicated search engine for scheduled flights, charter flights, last-minute flights, accommodation, ferries, cruises and all things travel.

Search Resources

About.Com   http://websearch.miningco.com
Now here's a find – a search site about search sites. Online search resources categorised by subject matter, plus features, tips and reviews.

Ask Jeeves –   http://www.
Through The Keyhole   askjeeves.com/docs/peek
See what other people are searching for, and how they phrase their searches. This page updates every thirty seconds with the twenty most recent search requests.

Boolean Searching   http://www.
on the Internet   nouveaux.com/Boolean.htm
A clear yet comprehensive primer in Boolean logic as it applies to searching the web. Good use of diagrams and plain English manage to get across complex mathematical concepts without pain.

Mata Hari   http://www.thewebtools.com/tutorial
A guide to effective searching on the Internet that manages to

pack in a lot of experience and knowledge into its pages. Well designed and well written.

ResearchBuzz   http://www.researchbuzz.com
What started out as a companion website to a book about searching online has developed into a highly focused centre for Internet researchers. Subjects covered range from news on new research tools through to tips on Boolean searching methods.

Search Engine Showdown   http://www.notess.com/search
Subtitled 'The Users' Guide to Web Searching', this website delivers pretty much on that promise. Plenty of comparative search engine reviews combined with statistics and strategies for searching success.

Search Engine Watch   http://www.searchenginewatch.com
A fascinating website absolutely packed with information about searching and search engines. Reviews, comparisons, hints, tips and advice on getting the best from your searches.

Seekhelp.Com   http://www.seekhelp.com
Click on the 'Learn to Search' button and you can discover how to use all of the major search engines to your best advantage. Also tips on searching for lost relatives.

The Spider's   http://www.
Apprentice   monash.com/spidap4.html
An easy-to-understand guide to how search engines work. Covering everything from keyword searching through to relevancy ranking and the use of meta tags.

WindWeaver's   http://www.
Search Guide   windweaver.com/searchguide.htm
A no-nonsense guide that sets out to show you which search tool to use and for what purposes.

3//THE TRAVELLER'S ADVISORY

A few years ago many people thought of the Internet as being the world's biggest library, then they realised it was far more than that. At a library you would have to make do with some dusty old almanac or atlas if you wanted a quick idea of the time zone, prevailing political climate and unit of currency in use in some far-off land. Even then, that information would most likely be dated and would certainly not have the capacity to update itself immediately as and when circumstances changed.

The Internet can help the savvy traveller with all those essentials you need to know before leaving for the travel agent's, let alone leave for the trip itself. No longer do you need to hang on the phone or wait in line to find out about the latest visa requirements for entry into a given country. Simply connect to an official embassy or consulate website and pull the information out of the ether at your convenience. Not sure whether the travel agent who sold you a holiday to some troubled shore was really telling the truth when you were assured that 'all the fighting is over and done with now'? See what the government departments that issue travel advisories and warnings have to say about the matter.

The Internet's interactivity and immediacy make a real difference to quality and accuracy of the information on offer. At the click of a mouse you can get up-to-date exchange rates and instant calculations of currency conversions. Travel insurance quotes can be garnered from more than one source, costs and benefits compared and an online purchase of cover made in less than the time it would take you to look up a broker in the phone book and make the call. City maps, often down to street-level detail can be summoned out of thin air and route maps between destinations displayed and printed free of charge.

We have grouped together some of the more useful sites under various common-sense headings. But there's a lot more out there. Take your Internet-searching knowledge gleaned from reading the previous chapter and put it to good use to find more sites that answer your particular pressing need.

//ADDRESS BOOK

Starting Points

Rec.Travel Library   http://www.travel-library.com
Despite the confusing name (the same as a series of Usenet newsgroups about travel), this is a site full of links to websites – a superbly indexed library that proves invaluable for quickly finding even the quirkiest of travel facts about any given destination.

Foreign and   http://www.
Commonwealth Office   fco.gov.uk/travel
The nice people at the Travel Advice Unit of the Consular Division of the Foreign and Commonwealth Office will tell you where you shouldn't be heading and why.

British Passport Office   http://open.gov.uk/ukpass/ukpass.htm
If you want to find out more about applying for or using a British passport then you've come to the right place. The real bonus here is that there are no queues or boorish officials.

BBC Weather Centre   http://www.bbc.co.uk/weather
Don't take any chances on the weather, wherever you are heading. The BBC packs UK and world information into a single, very comprehensive,very slick site.

Dictionaries and Translators

BabelFish   http://babelfish.altavista.com
If you happen across a website in a language you can't understand,

this is for you. Cut and paste the text and drop it into the BabelFish window for instant online translation.

Basic Phrases for   **http://www.**
Eastern Europe   **cusd.claremont.edu/~tkroll/EastEur**
A selection of essential language tips for Eastern European countries from Albania to Slovenia.

Cockney Online   **http://www.cockney.co.uk**
Don't feel like a foreigner in Britain's capital. Check out the authentic rhyming slang dictionary as compiled by this real East Ender.

Croatian Language   **http://www.**
Basic Phrases   **hr/hrvatska/language/CroLang.html**
From polite phrases to forms of address and complaining at a restaurant. If you want enough Croatian to get by as a tourist then look no further.

Indonesian and   **http://www.**
English Conversation   **iit.edu/~syafsya/searchconv.cgi**
Enter an English phrase or word and the Indonesian equivalent is spat out. Check the database of user requests that lists the Indonesian for such essential phrases as 'you're a bloody idiot'.

Japanese Online   **http://www.japanese-online.com**
Bone up on your Japanese lingo before you leave. Includes a very useful interactive English-Japanese dictionary.

Larry's Aussie Slang   **http://members.**
and Phrase Dictionary   **tripod.com/~thisthat/slang.html**
Visit this amusing and useful site and 'she'll be apples, mate'. Not for the easily offended, as Australian slang can be rather colourful.

Practical Turkish   **http://www2.egenet.tr/mastersj**
An audio library of spoken Turkish by subject matter. Turkish terms

of endearment could come in handy. Not so sure about the mathematical terms and phrases though.

Russian Dictionary   **http://www.visi.com/**
with Sounds and Images   **~swithee//dictionary/welcome.html**
A light-hearted website that teaches the pronunciation of common Russian words using pictures and audio files.

Spanish for the   **http://www.**
Virtual Student   **umr.edu/~amigos/Virtual**
Learn enough Español to get by when holidaying on the Costas. Best viewed 'poco a poco' as there's a lot here.

Survival Maltese   **http://www.fred.net/malta/malti.html**
Maltese language tutor aimed at the tourist. Sections include arrival, accommodation, eating out, shopping, the bank and the doctor, amongst others.

Travlang   **http://www.travlang.com**
An online phrasebook and language primer complete with audio to help you learn the lingo no matter where you are going.

Welsh Language   **http://www.**
Course   **cs.brown.edu/fun/welsh/Welsh.html**
A beginner's guide to speaking Welsh plus a Welsh spellchecker if you fancy trying to write in the language as well. But the Welsh do (usually) speak English too.

Embassies

One of the best ways to really discover the practical and political ins and outs of travelling to and around any particular country has always been to approach the respective embassy. Now you can do this without having to make an appointment and be fully protected by the anonymity of the Internet. It doesn't matter which country the embassy site is located in, as they all tend to link to each other and offer equally good advice to visitors of any nationality. Most have email addresses, so you can ask embassy officials if the exact problem you need resolving isn't answered, or the answer doesn't apply to your nationality.

EmbassyWeb   http://www.embpage.org
The contact details of some 50,000 embassies around the world can be found listed here. A searchable diplomacy database that contains street and email addresses as well as telephone numbers.

British Diplomatic   http://www.
Missions Finder   fco.gov.uk/links.asp
The websites of consulates, High Commissions and embassies representing British interests abroad are but a single click away from this well-laid-out directory.

Selected Embassies

Algeria	http://www.consalglond.u-net.com
Angola	http://www.angola.org
Argentina	http://www.argentina-embassy-uk.org
Armenia	http://www.armeniaemb.org
Australia	http://www.australia.org.uk
Austria	http://www.austria.org
Belgium	http://www.belgium-emb.org
Bosnia	http://www.bosnianembassy.org/index.html
Brazil	http://www.brasilemb.org
Britain	http://www.britainusa.com/bis/consular/consular.stm
Bulgaria	http://www.bulgaria-embassy.org
Cambodia	http://www.embassy.org/cambodia
Canada	http://www.cdnemb-washdc.org
China	http://www.chinese-embassy.org.uk
Columbia	http://www.colombiaemb.org
Czech Republic	http://www.czech.cz/washington

Denmark	http://www.denmarkemb.org
Ecuador	http://www.ecuador.org
Egypt	http://www.egypt-embassy.org.uk
Estonia	http://www.estonia.gov.uk
Finland	http://www.finland.org
France	http://www.ambafrance.org.uk
Georgia	http://www.darafeev.com/georgia.htm
Germany	http://www.german-embassy.org.uk
Ghana	http://www.ghana-embassy.org
Greece	http://www.greekembassy.org
Haiti	http://www.mnsinc.com/embassy
Hungary	http://www.hungaryemb.org
Iceland	http://www.iceland.org
India	http://www.indianembassy.org
Indonesia	http://www.prica.org
Iran	http://www.iran-embassy.org.uk
Ireland	http://www.irelandemb.org
Israel	http://www.israel-embassy.org.uk/london
Italy	http://www.embitaly.org.uk
Jamaica	http://www.caribbean-online.com/jamaica/embassy/washdc
Japan	http://www.embjapan.org.uk
Jordan	http://www.jordanembassyuk.gov.jo
Kuwait	http://embassyofkuwait.com
Latvia	http://www.latvia-usa.org
Lebanon	http://users.erols.com/lebanon
Lithuania	http://www.ltembassyus.org
Madagascar	http://www.embassy.org/madagascar
Mexico	http://www.demon.co.uk/mexuk
New Zealand	http://www.newzealandhc.org.uk
Norway	http://www.norway.org.uk/home_embassy.htm
Pakistan	http://www.pakistan-embassy.com
Philippines	http://www.philemb.demon.co.uk
Poland	http://www.poland-embassy.org.uk

Russia	http://www.russialink.couk.com/embassy/intro.htm
Slovenia	http://www.embassy-slovenia.org.uk
South Africa	http://www.southafricahouse.com
Sri Lanka	http://ourworld.compuserve.com/homepages/lanka
Sweden	http://www.swedish-embassy.org.uk/embassy
Switzerland	http://www.swissembassy.org.uk
Tanzania	http://www.tanzania-online.gov.uk
Turkey	http://www.turkishembassy-london.com
United States of America	http://www.usembassy.org.uk
Venezuela	http://www.embavenez-us.org

Exchange Rates

Currency Converter   http://www.oanda.com/converter/travel

Simple to use – just select a home and destination currency and let this site tell you how much your money is worth while abroad. Exchange rates are displayed in a 'cheat sheet' format for printing to take with you.

X-Rates   http://www.x-rates.com

An exchange rate calculator for the most popular of currencies. A gallery of money photographs – now you can see what a 10 ECU note looks like!

Cash Machines

MasterCard ATM Locator   http://www.mastercard.com/atm

Find the precise location of all 465,000 MasterCard cash machines around the world.

VISA ATM Locator   http://www.visa.com/pd/atm

If you need to find any of the world's 457,000 VISA hole-in-the-wall cash dispensers, start looking here.

General Financial Advice

Travelling With
Ed and Julie – Money
http://www.
twenj.com/moneyand.htm

A guide to money and foreign exchange in Western Europe. Covers everything from cash to credit cards, with a little bit of the Euro and travellers cheques thrown in.

Health

Centers for Disease Control
and Prevention
http://www.
cdc.gov/travel

A charming name for an essential reference. If you are contemplating travelling off the beaten track then check with this official US government oracle first.

Country by Country
Vaccination Guide
http://www.
tmvc.com.au/info10.html

A particularly useful website listing the necessary and recommended vaccinations when travelling to specific countries.

National Red Cross and
Red Crescent Societies
http://www.
ifrc.org

A directory of these wonderful organisations in 175 countries around the globe.

Travel Health Online
http://www.tripprep.com

A comprehensive database of health and safety issues for the world traveller. Everything from altitude sickness to yellow fever is covered in detail.

Tropical Medical Bureau
http://www.tmb.ie

An Irish clinic specialising in travel medicine, with plenty of free advice. Subjects covered include diarrhoea, insect bites and malaria protection.

World Health Organisation   **http://www.who.int/ctd**

The WHO Division of Control of Tropical Diseases to be precise. Discomfiting reading for the long-haul traveller, with a particularly alarming section on intestinal parasites.

First Aid For Travellers

Cuts, Bites   **http://www.**
and Stings   **lonelyplanet.com/health/cuts.htm**

Simple advice in dealing with cuts and scratches. Plus the bites and stings of assorted creatures including wasps, snakes, jellyfish, leeches and even bedbugs.

No Safe   **http://freenet.uchsc.edu/**
Tan   **2000/prevent/cancer/suntan/menu.html**

Before slipping on the thong and heading for the beach, you should read this. Maybe it will make you think twice about wanting to get bronzed this summer.

Travel Health Information Service   **http://travelhealth.com**

Everything you need to prepare for travel except the injections themselves! Arachnophobics beware: a lifelike animated spider crawls across this website.

Vessel Sanitation   **http://www.cdc.gov/nceh/**
Program   **programs/sanit/vsp/vsp.htm**

Thinking of a cruise? Check out what the US National Centre for Environmental Health has to say about the boat before you book.

Virtual   **http://www.vh.org/Providers/**
Hospital   **Textbooks/TravelMedicine**

General precautions and advice for the traveller, from 'orrible insects to sexually transmitted diseases.

Travel Sickness

Coping With Jet Lag   http://travelassist.com/mag/a81.html
Practical advice for anyone who flies a lot and finds themselves not functioning as well as they otherwise might.

Healthy Flying   http://www.flyana.com
Ah, the joys of air travel: air rage, ear pain, jet lag and dehydration. Don't miss the wonderful tale of the passenger who defecated on a first-class food cart.

Insurance

Screentrade   http://www.screentrade.co.uk
Instant online travel insurance from a selection of well-known companies. All accessible through this one-stop insurance shop.

Travel Bug Insurance   http://www.travel-pub.co.uk/insurance
Single-trip and annual quotes using the simple 'quote wizard'. Then buy the policy online using a secure server.

Travel Insurance Agency   http://www.travelinsurers.com
Specialising solely in travel insurance, this British-based company can provide instant travel cover using the secure online ordering system.

Travel Insurance Online   http://www. travelinsurance-online.com
A fast site with few frills to slow it down, but for UK residents only.

Maps

Atlapedia Online   http://www.atlapedia.com
Full-colour physical and political world maps that include key facts and statistics on all countries.

EuroShell   **http://www.shell.com/**
Planner   **euroshell/routeplanner**

Type in your starting point and destination in Europe and this site will return a map telling you how to drive there. Plus you get a detailed description that includes – can't imagine why – all the Shell petrol stations along the way.

MapBlast   **http://www.mapblast.com**

A USA map finder that has a useful feature to let you download maps on to WinCE handheld devices for ultimate portability.

Map Quest   **http://www.mapquest.com**

A fine selection of, mainly American, city maps on offer here. Plus a route-planning service for good measure.

MultiMap   **http://www.multimap.com/map/places.cgi**

An interactive atlas online. So far the world starts and stops in the UK, but with zoomable maps of Great Britain at street-level detail we are not complaining.

Street Map   **http://www.streetmap.co.uk**

Amazingly detailed British street maps that almost let you see your house!

Terraserver   **http://terraserver.microsoft.com**

A truly breathtaking experience that lets you home in on destinations from outer space by zooming in on the satellite images provided. It's not completely comprehensive, but the areas that are covered are simply wondrous to look at.

The Trip –   **http://www.**
Maps   **thetrip.com/usertools/maps/index**

An instant fix for US state and city maps. Just select from the drop-down menu and go.

Packing

Compleat Carry-On Traveller   http://www.oratory.com/travel
How to travel light and holiday out of one bag.

How To Put Your Stuff   http://www.webfoot.com/
In Your Luggage   travel/tips/pack.stuff.html
Stuffed full of tips on how best to pack what you need in the bag
you want.

Packing For A Snow   http://www. snowlink.
Sports Vacation   com/cool_pix/howpack.html
The essential guide as to what, and how, to pack for that winter
holiday.

Tips 4 Trips –   http://www.tips4trips.com/
Packing   Tips/packtips.htm
Ordinary travellers have submitted their essential tips for items you
shouldn't leave home without – like a small scented candle and a
Magic Marker.

Travelite FAQ   http://www.travelite.org
Another in-depth guide to packing all you need for that holiday
into just one bag. This could be the Next Big Thing.

Universal Packing List   http://www.henricson.se/mats/upl
Absolutely everything you need to take with you for the perfect
holiday.

Travel Warnings

*Sometimes events overtake holiday and business plans. If you
were due to travel to a destination in a troubled part of the world,
you would be well advised to check up on the safety situation
before you leave. Forewarned is forearmed, as someone must
have once said.*

ABC News: http://abcnews.go.com/
Dangerous Places   sections/world/dp/dp_intro.html
Special news reports on travel in some of the world's most dangerous places. Required reading for the adrenalin-seeking tourist.

Danger Finder   http://www.fieldingtravel.com/df
More essential reading for the adventurous traveller. Particularly strong on those remote areas that hold such an attraction for some hardy individuals.

Groupsource   http://www.
Travel Warnings   groupsource.com/twarnings.htm
Simply click on a link and you will automatically get an email informing you of any new warning issued by the US State Department.

Street Scams   http://cliffs.ucsd.edu/
of Barcelona   terry/barna/scams.html
An incredibly useful guide to all the things to watch out for when in Barcelona that could turn your holiday into a hell. Most of them involve different ways to part you from your money.

Travel Information and   http://www.dfait-maeci.gc.ca/
Advisory Reports   travelreport/menu_e.htm
Advisories and warnings on travel from the Canadian government.

US Department of State   http://travel.state.gov/
Travel Warnings   travel_warnings.html
The latest warnings about which destinations are deemed unsafe for travel, and why.

WEATHER

Met Office   http://www.meto.gov.uk
Don't leave the weather to chance. The UK Meteorological Office has all the latest local weather reports here.

Weather 24   **http://www.weather24.com**

A few minutes of online form filling and you can receive short-term weather forecasts by email, for free.

World Climate   **http://www.worldclimate.com**

Want to know what the weather is normally like in any of tens of thousands of locations around the globe? Just type in the name of the place and all will be revealed.

World Meteorological Organisation   **http://www.wmo.ch**

The global picture from this United Nations weather agency.

Storms and Worse

Hurricane Watch   **http://www.netcreations.com/hurricane**

This site keeps a close eye on hurricanes as they happen. You can even take a peek yourself thanks to the satellite images on display here.

Snow and Avalanche Center   **http://www.csac.org**

A non-profit organisation that keeps the world informed on the dangers of avalanches and features up-to-date snow reports.

Tracking El Niño   **http://www.pbs.org/wgbh/nova/elnino**

Everyone now knows the awesome power of El Niño, and the threat to property and life it holds. This site is dedicated to tracking the phenomenon and reporting back on its every move.

Weather Webcams

What better way of keeping an eye on the weather in foreign climes than to actually be able to watch the skies for yourself? Some of these webcams offer real-time feeds, that is to say that they refresh the images every few seconds, so you get as near to a live video image as possible. Most, however, are updated every ten minutes or so. And if the screen is black, it's probably night-time.

WebCam Central http://www. camcentral.com/Weather_Cams.html.
A huge index of weather webcams around the globe. Can be slow to load.

Amstercam http://www.amstercam.org
Live weather on your screen from Amsterdam.

Australian Surf Report http://www.realsurf.com
Surfing weather reports from Sydney's beaches.

Bermuda Cam http://www.bbsr.edu/Weather
The view from a webcam overlooking Castle Harbour. Click on the 'current conditions' link for the webcam.

Finland Weather Station http://193.167.57.7/weather
As seen from the Kymenlaaska Polytechnic.

Loch Ness Live Cam http://www. lochness.co.uk/livecam/index.html
Keep one eye on the weather and the other open for Nessie.

Mallorca http://www.mallorca-baleares.de/webcam.htm
Is the rain in this part of Spain falling mainly on the plain?

Milan Weather Reporter http://www.italyflash.com/italyflash/ shortt/meteo/wmilano.shtml
Live video of Milan's weather, and links to other major Italian cities.

Moscow Weather Cam http://www.paratype.com/camera/
Magnificent views from one of seven Moscow hills, looking towards the State University.

Tampa, Florida http://www.wtvt.com/skycam.htm
Located on top of the SkyTower Radar Dome, 250 feet above this Florida TV station and updated every five minutes.

Rio de Janeiro http://www.tvbox.com.br
The weather in seven different parts of Rio.

Swedish Weather   **http://www.ausys.se/vadret/**
This one is in Lijeholmen, Stockholm.

MISCELLANEOUS

Some seriously useful sites stubbornly refuse to sit easily in any category. Here is a brief pot pourri of travel advice sites.

Access Able   **http://www.access-able.com**
A site dedicated to the disabled traveller. A decent FAQ is accompanied by a directory of travel agents offering holidays for those with special needs.

Help For World Travellers   **http://www.kropla.com**
Offering advice on telephones, electricity and television standards around the world.

Air Miles   **http://www.airmiles.co.uk**
Is there anyone who doesn't collect air miles these days? The online site lets you check on your balance and check on the special offers available.

Judicial   **http://travel.state.gov/**
Assistance   **judicial_assistance.html**
How to get legal help, country by country. Intended for US citizens, but the advice is useful no matter where you hail from.

Manual of   **http://members.aol.com/**
Traffic Signs   **rcmoeur/signman.html**
The most commonly used traffic signs in the United States. Essential reading for anyone thinking of a fly-drive holiday for the first time.

Takeyourpet.Com   **http://takeyourpet.com**
All the advice you could need if you fancy taking Rover on holiday with you.

Pet Information   **http://www.**
Resource   **petlifeweb.com/Petinfo/petravel.htm**
Guides to pets in the air, on the road and travelling by foot.

Rabies Quarantine   **http://pw1.netcom.com/**
Policy   **~eholden/rabies.htm**
The rules on rabies quarantine for bringing dogs into the UK. Plus useful guides for taking dogs to other countries as well.

SeniorCom   **http://www.senior.com/travel**
Not a travel service for Mexicans, but an online magazine aimed squarely at Internet users aged 50 years and above.

Speedtrap Registry   **http://www.speedtrap.com**
Information on speed traps around the world, where they are located, how they work and what the fines are. Strictly for reference use only, obviously.

World Time Zone   **http://www.isbister.com/worldtime**
Irreplaceable. A website that will tell you the precise time anywhere in the world, in an instant.

Working Abroad

Travel   **http://www.travelnotes.org/**
Notes   **Travel/working_abroad.htm**
A very complete guide to working abroad. A good mixture of useful editorial and essential links to website resources.

International Study and   **http://www.**
Travel Centre   **istc.umn.edu/work**
Helps students combine work and travel, for those long summer holidays.

AllAbroad.com   **http://www.allabroad.com**
Another site mainly for students, with a searchable database.

US Experience
Handbook.com

http://www.us.
experience-handbook.com

Very serious, very grown-up book with all the information you need about salary packages, whether it's a really good move, and more disconcerting considerations.

4//DESTINATIONS

For a growing number of travellers the journey doesn't begin at the airport but rather it starts on the Internet. Hardly surprising when you consider the sheer scale of the information that can be uncovered on the World Wide Web using nothing more complicated than a mouse click or two.

Most countries have an official home on the web, usually provided by the tourist board or local equivalent. Indeed, what with the Internet being so good at providing lists, it should come as little surprise that there's a Tourism Offices Worldwide Directory site that provides links to just about every tourist board online, as well as contact details for those that aren't. Government pages warn of passport and visa requirements, while embassy sites issue advisories regarding political unrest in foreign climes – as detailed in Chapter 3.

The canny reader, however, won't settle for the official line alone, no matter how accurate and uncoloured that may be. Nor need they, with the multitude of alternative sites that paint a down-to-earth picture of the countries concerned. From the polished professionalism of the Lonely Planet or Rough Guide sites, to the passionate parlez of a local hotelier touting for business, the voices on the Internet are many.

In keeping with the finest traditions of the net, it's only proper that some of the best information comes from the unlikeliest of sources. The CIA World Fact Book, for example, offers an encyclopaedic level of country-specific knowledge. After all, if the spies can't gather such authoritative information then who can? The answer to that question would appear to be Microsoft, whose vast Expedia service combines travelogues and magazine-style resort guides with interactive online flight, hotel and car rental booking facilities.

The websites listed in this chapter will all help unravel the secrets of the destinations concerned, listed by geographical region for your convenience. We've selected a mixed bag of official tourist-board and government-sponsored sites, and added the best unofficial sites provided by tour operators and experienced travellers. All provide a strong local flavour of the destination in question.

//ADDRESS BOOK

Starting Points

CIA World   **http://www.odci.gov/cia/**
Fact Book   **publications/factbook**
Don the sunglasses, type in the longwinded address, and prepare to be impressed by the information collected by the men in black.

Tourism Offices Worldwide Directory   **http://www.towd.com**
A comprehensive guide to more than 1,700 official tourist information offices around the world.

TravelDex   **http://www.traveldex.co.uk**
Super-fast site for finding out about the destination of your choice.

World Travel Guide   **http://www.travel-guides.com**
Click on the maps until you arrive at your virtual destination, then discover all you need to know.

AFRICA – EAST

Ethiopia

Library of Congress – Ethiopia Study   http://lcweb2.loc.gov/frd/cs/ettoc.html

The history, culture and people are all explored and explained in depth by this US Library of Congress special.

Addis Ababa Home Page   http://www.macalester.edu/~kshively

This website was produced as a geography class project by a student in Minnesota. Although it's slow to load, it does provide a good overview of the Ethiopian capital.

Kenya

Visit Kenya   http://visit-kenya.com

A virtual tour of Kenyan hotels, a safari booking service, restaurant guide and travel brochure all rolled into one. And that's just the first page.

Jambo Mombassa   http://www.africaonline.co.ke

A good all-round look at Mombassa. Travel and tourism are well catered for, but there are also links to local businesses to provide a true local flavour.

Virtual Nairobi   http://www.kenyaweb.com/vnairobi/

Everything is well covered on this website, from the best places to eat in Nairobi to the best day trips out of the Kenyan capital.

Mauritius

Mauritius Welcomes You   http://www.mauritius.net

The Mauritius Tourism Promotion Authority politely invite you to their island, and at the same time inform you about the weather, food, sights, hotels and visa requirements.

Sudan

Al Sudan   **http://www.sudan.net**
Everything about Sudan, from tourist information to statistics, politics and who's who.

Zanzibar

Zanzibar Travel Network   **http://www.zanzibar.net**
The best-kept secret in the Indian Ocean revealed. Look beyond the unspoilt beaches and explore the stone town that has changed little in 200 years.

AFRICA – NORTH

Algeria

Mifta Shamali   **http://i-cias.com/m.s/algeria**
A very colourful site, both in design and content, with an exploration of the bustle of Algiers to the architectural beauty of the Hippo Regius. It's probably the closest you'll get; actual travel in Algeria is heavily restricted due to internal conflict.

Casbah Alger   **http://www.ovpm.org/ovpm/sites/aalger.html**
A useful and brief site that is actually very straightforward with its information despite section headings like 'Urban Morphology'.

Egypt

Egyptian Ministry of Tourism   **http://www.touregypt.net**
Skip the introduction from the Minister of Tourism and you soon discover plenty of Egyptian culture, economics and tourist attractions. The living history of ancient Egypt, as brought alive in the 'Pharaonic Village' section, is particularly impressive.

Alexandria 2000   **http://www.alexandria2000.com**
Sightseeing guides, weather reports, photos and the online

periodical 'Alexandria 2000 Times' to keep you up to date with the latest travel news in the region.

Cairo Guide   http://www.cairo-guide.com

An excellent guide to the capital. Complete with atmospheric images and music, and enough information to break a camel's back.

Luxor   http://www-ceg.ceg.uiuc.edu/~haggag/luxor.html

An overview of Luxor's many monuments and temples. Plus links to other Luxor-related websites.

Libya

Find Out More   http://www.
About Libya   geocities.com/Athens/8744/mylinks1.htm

The personal audio greeting from Colonel Qaddafi may not be to everyone's taste, but the rest of this information-packed site is very useful indeed.

A Virtual Kazdoura   http://tripoli-
in Tripoli   city.org/kazdoura01.html

A Kazdoura is a tour, and this charming site is a virtual tour of Libya's capital in a series of pages.

Morocco

Morocco Bound   http://tayara.com/club/mrocbd1.htm

We will forgive the weakly punning title, as this is a veritable treasure chest for the independent traveller. One thing you quickly learn is that camels are your best friends in Morocco.

Tunisia

ArabNet   http://www.
Tunisia   arab.net/tunisia/tunisia_contents.html

Extremely interesting and exhaustive site covering Tunisia from every possible angle. The history and people right through to visas and customs regulations, plus an essential guide to transport.

AFRICA – SOUTHERN

Republic of Angola   http://www.angola.org
The official website of this African republic. Tourism isn't high on the agenda, but there's enough information here to satisfy any would-be traveller's thirst for knowledge.

Virtual Lobito   http://www.geocities.com/TheTropics/4104
A virtual train ride to the city of Lobito. Worth waiting for, even though this web page does chug along a bit slowly.

The Malawi Tourism   http://www.
Website   malawi-tourism.com
Malawi means 'reflected light', just one of the many things you'll discover at the Ministry of Tourism website.

Namibia Travel Online   http://www.natron.net/etour.htm
They call Namibia 'Africa's Gem', so polish up on accommodation, car hire and safaris here. Or just sit back and enjoy a pictorial tour of the country instead.

South Africa

Southern Africa Places   http://www.places.co.za
Its troubled past now behind it, South Africa is a prime tourist destination, as this well-laid-out and easily navigable site demonstrates.

Cape   http://www.capeconnected.
Connected   co.za/travframe.htm
A traveller's guide to Cape Town that can be slow to load, but is ultimately rewarding, with links to cover everything from fishing to museums and city transport.

Durbanet   http://durbanet.aztec.co.za/tourism

A useful tourism directory that links you to game lodges, nature reserves, accommodation, car rental and tour operators in Durban.

Time Out Guide to   http://www.
Johannesburg   timeout.com/johannesburg

The essential guide to anyone who wants to know what's on and where in Johannesburg.

Destination Pretoria   http://www.visitpretoria.co.za

An odd-looking site, with lots of white space and just a few small colour photos. Street maps, shopping guides and all the usual accommodation and sightseeing stuff.

Swaziland

Tourism in Swaziland   http://www.swazi.com/tourism

Discover the Swazi cultural village, the Royal Experience, the horse trails at Mlilwane and more.

Zimbabwe

GORP – Zimbabwe Tourist   http://www.gorp.com/gorp/
Information   location/africa/zimbabwe/zimbinfo.htm

Essential travel information about visas, health, currency and transport – and good links to coverage of Zimbabwe's national parks and scenic wonders.

AFRICA – WEST

Cameroon

Postcards from   http://www.geocities.com/
Cameroon   TheTropics/Shores/4051/menu_eng.htm

An unofficial pictorial tour of the country that reveals otherwise hidden treasures such as the Chieffery of Bandjoun, built two centuries ago as a symbol of the power and authority of the chief.

Destination   http://www.lonelyplanet.
Chad   com.au/dest/afr/cha.htm
The Republic of Chad laid bare for the would-be visitor. All you
need to know and some things you probably don't.

Lycos City Guide   http://cityguide.lycos.com/
to N'Djamena   africa/westcentral_africa/TCDNDjamena.html
The best, and indeed one of the only, online guides to the capital
city of Chad.

Congo

Congo Pages   http://www.congo-pages.org/welcome.htm
The real-life and culture of the Congolese people. Don't miss the
culinary delights and the look at this lush country's extraordinary
wildlife.

Gambia

GambiaNet   http://www.gambianet.com
Something for everyone, whether you want basic travel
information or detailed daily local and national news bulletins.

Ghana

An Introduction   http://www.
to Ghana   interknowledge.com/ghana/index.html
Not much in the way of imagery or fancy design. Just the facts on
the climate, the history and the people of Ghana.

Nigeria

Motherland Nigeria   http://www.motherlandnigeria.com
Do not adjust your browsers! Webmaster Olubunmi Boomie O has
created a very colourful website. Soak up the Nigerian atmosphere
– and the information.

ANTARCTICA

Rob Holme's Cool   http://www.
Antarctic Stuff   theice.org/faq.html
A complete FAQ offering answers to such questions as 'Where do
you go to the bathroom?' and 'How cold does it get?'

Lonely Planet –   http://www.
Destination Antarctica   lonelyplanet.com/dest/ant/ant.htm
The Lonely Planet guide to 14.25 million freezing cold square
kilometres. In this case the 'off the beaten track' section is probably
superfluous.

Glacier   http://www.glacier.rice.edu
Unique insights into arctic life and answers to all your questions
about ice.

Polar   http://www-bprc.mps.ohio-
Pointers   state.edu/polarpointers/Antarctica.html
A set of links to other sites covering all aspects of polar life from the
biology to the weather.

Virtual Antarctica   http://www.terraquest.com/antarctica
The first exploration of Antarctica to report back live to the
Internet. Terraquest is essential reading if you fancy a trip to one of
the world's last great wildernesses.

ASIA – CENTRAL

Afghanistan

Afghanistan Online   http://www.afghan-web.com
The whole Afghan kit and caboodle, from geography to local
sports news. No mention of large hairy dogs though.

Turkey

Daily Turkish News http://www.turkishpress.com

Still recovering from the devastating earthquake of August 1999, the Turkish Press web pages will keep you informed of progress in rebuilding a shattered country.

ASIA – SOUTH

Bangladesh

Virtual Bangladesh http://www.virtualbangladesh.com

As well as a grand tour, Virtual Bangladesh serves up recipes, live chat and up-to-the-minute news.

India

Official India http://www.tourindia.com

Discover the beauty of this vast country with the help of the Government of India Tourist Office. From a photo gallery to the national anthem, it's all here to take away.

Project Cyber Assam http://www.assam.org

A truly appalling name for a truly useful website. Known as the land of flowers, not tea as you might expect, Assam is full of surprises and most of them can be found described and photographed here.

DelhiGate http://www.delhigate.com/main.htm

As busy on the eye as the city itself, with transportation, accommodation, weather reports and restaurant guides. Unexpected pluses include advice for women tourists and warnings about bad businesses.

Welcome to Goa! http://www.goacom.com

A very slick website that introduces Goa by way of accommodation and tourist traps as you might expect. But also plenty of surprises like the recipes, religions and Goan village showcases.

Gujurat Online http://www.gujaratonline.com

A guide to one of the most industrialised states of Western India. Listen to authentic Gujurati music and explore the links to the people, culture and tourist attractions of the region.

Library Kashmir http://www.clas.ufl.edu/users/
Virtual gthursby/kashmir/travel.htm

A po-faced, no-frills directory of links to websites detailing geography and travel in this much-disputed region of India.

Maps of http://mapsofindia.
Maharashtra com/maps/maharashtra

This one's a real find, especially if you like looking at maps. Not just of the topography of the region itself, but road maps and railway network maps as well.

Punjab Online http://www.punjabonline.com

Well-designed site packed with information. A search engine and navigation bar make accessing this vast resource easy.

Rajasthan http://www.rajasthan-
Tourism tourism.com/rajtourism

The official government-operated tourism site for Rajasthan, permeated by pictures of camels. Massive indexes of travel information from tourism maps and destination directories through to fairs and festivals.

Tourism of http://www.gl.
West Bengal umbc.edu/~achatt1/tour.html

Nicely presented site featuring tourist spots navigable by district using image-map hotspots.

Nepal

Nepal Home Page   **http://www.info-**
Travel Directory   **nepal.com/nhp/travel**
Trek over to this country guide for lots of useful information about
this landlocked, mountainous country.

Pakistan

Pakistan   **http://www.alephx.com/pakistan**
The government, the economy, the cities are all covered on this
eponymous site. It's the captivating pictures that stay with you
though.

Islamabad Net   **http://www.islamabad.net**
A suitably impressive and comprehensive site for Pakistan's capital
city. A directory-style interface offers easy access to wide-ranging
information resources.

Welcome to Karachi   **http://www.alephx.org/karachi**
An excellent directory of restaurants, shops, places of interest,
hotels and happenings. The numbering of questions in the FAQ
would confuse anyone: 1 ... 2 ... 3 ... 107 ... 110 ... 123 ... and so on.

Lahore   **http://www.alephx.com/**
Places   **lahore/html/place.html**
Divided into historic and modern Lahore, this website presents the
intriguing contrasts of Pakistan old and new.

Geography and Provinces   **http://www.rpi.edu/dept/union/**
of Peshawar   **paksa/www/html/pakistan/peshawar.html**
Founded 2,000 years ago by the Kushan Kings of Gandhara –
Peshawar, not this website. An excellent introduction for the
would-be tourist.

Quetta http://www.alephx.com/quetta

The capital of Baluchistan, Quetta is the legendary stronghold of the western frontier. The Quetta tribesmen are known for friendliness and hospitality, a tradition echoed by this website.

Sri Lanka

Ari Withanage's http://members.
Sri Lanka Homepage tripod.co.uk/withanage

A personal gateway to the paradise island of Sri Lanka, which doesn't gloss over its political instability but does strive to paint a picture that goes beyond the headlines.

ASIA – SOUTH-EASTERN

Cambodia

Cambodia Web http://www.cambodia-web.net

The Kingdom of Cambodia revealed in maps, history, culture, a Cambodian newspaper and a gallery of paintings and pho-tographs. There's even a job vacancy section if you're planning to stay there.

China

Tour in China http://www.ihep.ac.cn/tour/china_tour.html

A no-nonsense tour of China and its provinces. Maybe not the most exciting of site designs, but what it lacks in lustre it makes up for in content.

The Beijing Page http://www.flashpaper.com/beijing

A tourist guide to Beijing, and a directory of the region's food, industry and other diversions.

HongKong.Com http://www.hongkong.com/en

For visitors to Hong Kong this tongue-twisting site is the number one site, and no phooey.

Inner Mongolia   http://www.
Autonomous Region   bupt.edu.cn/regnet/inmon.html
The third largest of Chinese provinces is featured in this home-grown website covering agriculture, economics, transportation and city guides.

Shanghai City   http://www.
Guide   worldexecutive.com/cityguides/shanghai
Part of the World Executive hotel discount guide, this virtual tour of Shanghai includes city maps, travel tips and places to visit.

Welcome to Sichuan   http://www.scsti.ac.cn/En/tourism.html
All the major tourist attractions in this region – the Yangtze Three Gorges, Bamboo Forest and the Jianmen Pass – are covered here, if somewhat briefly.

Japan

Japan Information Network   http://jin.jcic.or.jp
An interactive atlas and a stunning virtual tour of Japan.

Hiroshima Home Page   http://www.hiroshima.org
Remembered for all the right reasons, we should never forget the legacy of Hiroshima. However, this site combines that history with up-to-date tourism information.

Fukuoka Now!   http://www.fukuoka-now.com
OK, we admit the school playground naughty name attracted our attention to this site. Once you get here, though, you discover an excellent magazine-style guide to what's on and where in the Fukuoka prefecture of Japan.

Kyoto Media   http://www.joho-
Station   kyoto.or.jp/~english/index_e.html
Delightfully named sections such as 'Essential Information for Foreigners' contain perplexing FAQs like 'Why don't you enjoy Pachinko?' and 'Money used for congratulations and funerals'.

Nagasaki Regional Information

http://www.nagasaki-u.ac.jp/nagasaki-city/nagasaki.html

A mixture of English and Japanese language information provided by the Nagasaki University Campus Information Network.

Wonderful Osaka

http://www.geocities.com/Hollywood/Screen/3033

Quite the politest welcome to a website, complete with bowing Japanese gentlemen. The enjoyment continues inside with a guide to entertainment, food and language from a proud local.

Tokyo Meltdown

http://www.bento.com/tleisure.html

A wonderfully simple site that covers Tokyo inside out. A thousand restaurants, a directory of record shops, useful telephone numbers and more.

Laos

Discovering Laos

http://www.laoembassy.com/discover

Let the Lao People's Democratic Republic embassy introduce you to the land of a million elephants – their description, not ours.

Malaysia

Visit Malaysia

http://www.tourism.gov.my

A beautiful website for a beautiful country, but be warned that it can be as slow to load as a removal man on a tea break.

Tibet

Tibetan Journey

http://www.schneuwly.com

A travelogue in words and pictures of one man's journey through Tibet with a bagful of film and pot noodles.

Philippines

Fil Info

http://www.filipino.com

7,107 islands of fun, and everything you could possibly need to know about them is to be found here on a single site.

Singapore

Unorthodox **http://www.geocities.**
Singapore **com/TheTropics/7222/main.html**
A compellingly honest insider's guide from a Chinese Singapore citizen called Robin.

Taiwan

Taiwanese Tourism Bureau R.O.C **http://www.tbroc.gov.tw**
The official tourism bureau site, made in Taiwan naturally enough. Good design and informative content.

Thailand

Thailand: The Big Picture **http://www.nectec.or.th**
Just about managing to deliver on its promise by providing links to web pages that will answer every query about the country.

Vietnam

Vietnam Web **http://home.vnn.vn**
A mind-boggling array of cultural and practical information about a country that has turned from battleground into sought-after holiday destination.

THE CARIBBEAN

The Anguilla Online **http://www.turq.**
Tourist Guide **com/anguilla**
Covering just 35 square miles, they call Anguilla 'Tranquillity in Blue', and this turquoise site superbly illustrates why.

Bahamas Online **http://thebahamas.com**
Like much else in the Caribbean this website can be slow moving but ultimately rewarding. Plenty of tourist interest wrapped up in an easily navigable and typically tropical design.

Always Dreaming of　　　　　　　　　http://www.
Bermuda　　　　　　　　　　　　dreamingofbermuda.bm
So much information is packed on to the index page that it can be hard to find your way around. Persistence pays off, though, with probably the most in-depth Bermudan tourist resource online.

BVI Welcome Online　　　　　　http://www.bviwelcome.com
Lodgings, shopping and more, all packed into this colourful Caribbean magazine site. Published in conjunction with the British Virgin Islands Tourist Board.

Cayman Islands Tourism　　　　http://www.caymanislands.ky
Beautiful photography helps bring the Cayman Islands to life on this official tourism site. Check out the turtle farm and stingray city while you are here.

The Cuban Connection　　　　　　　http://www.cuba.tc
Men with beards, big cigars, a last bastion of communism and home to fine beaches, swaying palm trees and extraordinary architecture. This English- and Spanish-language site acts as both an information and travel-booking gateway.

Welcome to　　　　　　　　　　　　http://www.
Curaçao　　　interknowledge.com/curacao/prohome.htm
Plenty of diving and cruising information on this official tourist board site, and guides to the best nightlife, restaurants and shops.

Grenada – Official　　　　　　　　　http://www.
Travel Guide　　　　　　　　　　travelgrenada.com
Maps, yachting information, villa rentals and sightseeing advice. There's a very nice section for honeymooners who might want to stay at the wonderfully named Flamboyant Hotel.

Island Connoisseur　　http://www.caribbeansupersite.com/haiti
Essential reading to prepare for a visit to Haiti. From the flora and

fauna to travel hints and destination guides. Don't miss it whatever voodoo.

Virtual Jamaica   **http://www.virtualjamaica.com**
A photographic tour of the country especially for those who want the big picture. Just point your mouse at the map, anywhere from Kingston to Montego Bay.

Citiview of Puerto Rico   **http://www.spiderlink.net/citiview/**
Features include a dictionary to learn the lingo, emergency phone number directory and a poets' room, promoting local culture.

Accenting St. Kitts and Nevis   **http://www.stkitts-nevis.com**
Official guide to this two-island tropical paradise. There's even a newsgroup feature so you can chat with other travellers and locals alike.

St Lucia: **http://www.multimania.com/**
A Guided Tour   **schmittg/index_a.html**
An easy-to-navigate site that comes without frills but with plenty of useful information including maps of the island and the main town, Castries.

Jewels of the Caribbean   **http://www.svgtourism.com**
Whether you are more interested in diving and sailing or dining and dancing there will be something of interest at this beautifully presented official tourism site covering St Vincent and the Grenadines.

Welcome to Trinidad & Tobago   **http://www.visittnt.com**
A slick government-sponsored site with a 'what's new' ticker and pages of straightforward advice on accommodation and island enjoyment.

Turks & Caicos Online   **http://milk.tciway.tc**
Email addresses of islanders and a downloadable screensaver, as well as the usual comprehensive island information.

US Virgin Islands   http://usvi-info.com

A pleasingly simple site that's split into separate sections: visitor's guide, marine guide, film and video guide, business guide and island facts.

CENTRAL AND SOUTH AMERICA

Argentina

Argentina Tour   http://www.argentour.com

Once you've fought your way past the different language options the site reveals itself as a useful guide to travelling in Argentina. There's even video footage of some of the tours arranged by the site hosts.

Belize

A Belize Online Tourist and   http://www.
Investment Guide   belize.com

Quite a mouthful when the Belize Travel Directory would be just as accurate. Natural assets and offshore banking facilities nestle side by side – and the chance of an online chat with the locals.

Bolivia

An Insider's Guide to Bolivia   http://www.bolivia-tourism.com

Bolivia's past, its tourist attractions, its major cities and present-day activities.

Brazil

BrazilInfo   http://www.brazilinfo.com/index_en.htm

Football, beaches, beautiful people and carnivals. You could say it's Brazil in a nutshell.

Chile

Chile: A Country of Opportunities http://www.chile.cl
A feature-packed and readable site – as long as you click the English-language icon.

Colombia

Latin American Student http://www.colostate.edu/Orgs/LASO/
Organisation Guide to Colombia Colombia/colombia.html
A very detailed guide that takes a while to load because its on one very long page indeed.

Costa Rica

Costa Rica's Travel Net http://www.centralamerica.com
The oldest and largest Costa Rican travel and tourism site on the web. Nice photo gallery.

Ecuador

Welcome to Ecuador http://perso.easynet.fr/~lsoulie
Ecuador explored by this French site, which is also available in English.

Guatemala

Homepage Guatemala http://www.guatemala.travel.com.gt
The country of eternal spring, apparently. More practical facts can be found on this official tourist board site that incorporates a search engine and a photo tour.

Honduras

Honduras.Com http://www.honduras.com
One site but many avenues allowing you to see, chat, travel and explore Honduras. Beaches, cities, ruins and Honduran football.

Panama

Panama Travel　　　　　　　　http://www.panamatravel.com
What to do and where to go in Panama, and a virtual museum of the Panama Canal.

Paraguay

About Com's　　　　　　http://gosouthamerica.about.com/
guide to Paraguay　　　　　　　　msubParaguay.htm
Dozens of indexed links to sites covering every aspect of Paraguayan life for both the tourist and the business traveller alike.

Peru

Peru Explorer　　　　　　　　http://www.peru-explorer.com
A well-designed and feature-packed website that covers Inca heritage and river rafting equally well. And the 'chirping parrots' title banner is a joy.

EUROPE

Austria

Austrian National　　　　　　　　　　http://www.
Tourist Guide　　　　　　abserv.co.at/abserv/tourist
Upper Austria, Salzburg, Carinthia, Styria, Vienna and the Tyrol. A directory of 'castle hotels' is typical of the little detailed information available at this site.

Imperial Cities –　　　　　　　　http://www.anto.com/
Innsbruck　　　　　　　　　　innsbruck.html
A well-illustrated, if brief, guide to the old capital of the Tyrol.

Salzburg City Tourist Information　　http://www.salzburginfo.at
The city of both Mozart and The Sound of Music, covered in a 360-degree photo tour – plus an A-Z directory of tourist information.

Belgium

Belgium.com http://www.living-in-belgium.com

Whether you are holidaying, just passing through or planning on working in Belgium, check out this guide for and by expatriates.

Antwerp City Guide http://myplace.to.be/antwerp

A visitor's guide to Antwerp, written and designed by local foreigners.

Brussels.com http://www.brussels.com

Capital of the European Union, Brussels is well served by this extensive city guide. Travel agencies, hotels, restaurants and entertainment listings are all here.

Bulgaria

Bulgaria.com http://www.travel-bulgaria.com

History, tradition, culture, nature – the complete Bulgarian travel experience is here. However, some people might just be able to come up with a riposte to the question posed here: 'Bulgaria – why not?'

Czech Republic

Czech Tourism Pages http://czech-tourism.com

There's more to the Czech Republic than just Prague and its famous bridges, you know.

Czeching Out http://ourworld.compuserve.
Prague com/homepages/RJWinters/prague.htm

A travelogue and mini-guide to Prague. And its famous bridges…

Cyprus

Cyprus Tourism Organisation http://www.cyprustourism.org

'Irresistible for 9,000 years', we are told. We think they mean Cyprus rather than the website.

Croatia

Croatian Tourist   http://www.
Information Service   htz.hr/home.htm

The Adriatic is the cleanest sea in the Mediterranean, it says here.
A very comprehensive directory to all things Croatian.

Denmark

Visit Denmark   http://www.dt.dk

The ultimate Euro-guide to Denmark, with ten different language
versions. And you'll want to customise the events page to suit your
personal tastes. One of the most professional tourism sites we've
encountered.

Tourist in   http://copenhagen.now.dk/
Copenhagen   english/kbh/turist/oversigt.html

A simple but effective guide to getting there, travelling around the
town and the best places to exchange currency.

England

Local Government   http://www.
Web Index   oultwood.com/localgov/england.htm

Websites about England as a whole, rather than the UK, are
amazingly difficult to find. This is a gem, though, with a clickable
map giving access to local government and council sites to get a
real grass-roots tour of the country.

Virtual   http://www.
Birmingham   colintonmas.demon.co.uk/Index.html

The UK's second city photographed in 360-degree panoramas.
Almost better than the real thing.

Blackpool Hotels   http://www.
Directory   blackpool-hotels.co.uk

Find one of Blackpool's famous landladies online, see what's on at the theatre and send an electronic postcard, even if you've never been there.

Cambridge Virtual City   http://www.worldwidecity.com/cambridge/index.html

A good tourist guide in spite of the eclectic design and navigation system. Very strong on transport, in case you don't have a bicycle.

City of Derby   http://www.derbycity.com

Excellent presentation matched by interesting content such as a section on Derby ghosts and another on its museums and theatres. If it's happening in Derby then the chances are you'll find out about it here.

This Is London   http://www.thisislondon.com

A suitably sprawling site for the capital city provided by the London Evening Standard newspaper. Everything from days out to a guide to Royal London and detailed directories of places to eat and drink.

Manchester Online   http://www.manchesteronline.co.uk/index.html

Your opportunity to become a virtual Mancunian by way of this in-depth and entertaining website. As well as all the local news and tourist info, you can also view 1,000 images of Manchester or choose where to go for a good night out.

Newcastle City Council   http://www.newcastle.gov.uk

It's nice to see local councils producing such impressive websites. This one uses 'quick lists' navigation bars to help you find the information you need.

Welcome to Oxford   http://www.oxfordcity.co.uk

A virtual guide with city maps, road information and access advice for disabled visitors. There's also a useful diary section that reports what's on in town every day.

This is Plymouth http://www.thisisplymouth.co.uk
Steeped in history, blacked out by the 1999 eclipse and home of the Evening Herald, creators of this very detailed local web guide. It's worth jumping straight to the A-Z format content index if you are in a hurry.

Made in Sheffield http://www.made-in-sheffield.com
Made famous by The Full Monty, there's plenty more to Sheffield than a bunch of men removing their underpants, as this refreshingly clean site proves.

Windsor – http://www.demon.
The Guide co.uk/GRA/eat@j/windsor/intro.html
What to do, where to eat and sleep, where to go in Royal Windsor. Part of the Eat@Joe's city guide series, with clean and easily navigable pages.

Historic York http://www.salvonet.com/yorkweb/walk
An innovative site that takes you on a virtual tour of historic York on foot. Through winding alleys and down cobbled streets, take in the sights as you go – and no blisters!

Estonia

Estonian Tourist Board http://www.tourism.ee
A largely black and white home page sets the monotone for the rest of the site. No-nonsense design with easy access to all the usual tourist information.

Finland

Virtual Finland http://virtual.finland.fi
News, history, culture and travel facts and plenty of trumpet blowing about famous Finns.

City of Helsinki http://www.hel.fi/english
The emphasis here is on practical help for visitors. So there's full

timetable information for all forms of internal transport, maps of the city and even tram routes.

France

Tourism in France   http://www.tourisme.fr/us/index.htm
Very fast, very informative, very French and very official. This French Tourism Office website is spoilt only by some appalling English. What on earth do they mean by 'a selection of unwonted stays to discover France'?

A Tour of   http://www.
Bordeaux   bordeaux.com/tour/tour.htm
Where to stay and where to eat, but above all, how to take in all the vineyards of the region.

Lourdes Official   http://www.lourdes-
Website   france.com/bonjour.htm
Use the drop-down menus to select which pages you want to read. Your choices include accommodation, pilgrimages, cures and miracles and separate homepages for both the town and the shrine sanctuary.

Discovering Lyon   http://www.ec-lyon.fr/tourisme/Lyon
Food and drink play a big part here, but it's also good for cinema and entertainment listings.

Beyond the   http://www.
French Riviera   beyond.fr/villages/marseille.html
The fascinating history of Marseilles and the answers to all the important tourism questions – like 'Where is the fish market?'

Welcome to Nice   http://www.alpix.com/nice
Meet the locals, soak up the audio ambience and dive headlong into impressive panoramas of the town. If you have the necessary plug-in then your browser can even take you on a virtual reality 3D flyover.

Paris Anglophone   http://www.paris-anglo.com/index.html
City tours, Parisian restaurant guides and a virtual tour of the town. Pop into the FrancoFile forums if you fancy a chat with locals or fellow travellers.

Welcome to Toulouse   http://www.mairie-toulouse.fr
Patchy design and content, but there's good coverage of culture, leisure and transport and some useful city maps.

Hungary

Hungarian   http://www.
Home Page   fsz.bme.hu/hungary/homepage.html
An introduction to Europe's crossroads, as seen by assorted Hungarian home pages.

Budapest.Com   http://www.budapest.com
A nice slide show of the Hungarian capital's sights and a live chat room, plus the usual hotel, restaurant and museum guides.

Germany

German National   http://www.
Tourist Board   germany-tourism.de
A very friendly site designed with the new visitor in mind. Major events listings through to the year 2003 and a 'facets of travelling' section covering all types of travel from youth hostelling to business trips.

SIS Berlin   http://www.berlin.de
First click on the 'English Content' link and then move on to the 'Tourist Centre'. One of those by now almost mandatory 360-degree virtual tours, plus tips for first-time visitors and a directory of 300 hotels in the capital.

Frankfurt Information   http://www.frankfurt.de
Overloaded with pictures on the index page, so it takes a while

to get going. But there's plenty of English language tourist information about the home of the Euro.

Hamburg Tourist Board   http://www.hamburg-tourism.de

Like many of the German tourism sites, this is slow to load and heavy on imagery, but the interactive city map provides an excellent tour of the town. It almost makes you feel like a Hamburger.

Stadt Leipzig   http://www.leipzig.de/engl.htm

Untypical in its low-bandwidth design and speedy loading times. As good as the rest for the information provided, including history and culture, business and tourism.

There is more to Munich   http://www.munich-tourist.de

More than what, they don't actually say. What we do discover is a website fully loaded with places to go and information on the transport to get you there.

Welcome to Stuttgart   http://www.stuttgart-tourist.de

Easily navigated thanks to being broken down into broad-content categories. The section on transport is typically complete, covering air and train as well as motorways and bus journeys.

Greece

InfoXenios   http://www.areianet.gr/infoxenios

An award-winning tourism site, apparently. It's the official guide to Greece and is encyclopaedic in its coverage.

Athens Survival Guide   http://www.athensguide.com

One man's experiences of travel to and within Athens have been transformed into this incredibly comprehensive guide to Athens. The newspapers, the soup, the taxi services, the flea markets, the lot. Print it out and take it with you.

Welcome to the Ionian Islands   http://www. ionian-islands.com

A holiday planner for anyone considering travel to Korfu, Paxoi,

Leykada, Ithaki, Kefalonia or Zakynthos. Well, mainly Zakynthos at the time of writing, although work is underway on the rest.

Welcome to Cephalonia   http://www.geocities.
Tourist Board   com/Athens/Agora/6062
A beautiful island and an interesting guide. Spectacular images from outer space, courtesy of NASA, mingle with more down-to-earth panoramic images of villages and beauty spots.

Rhodes –   http://www.webcom.
The City   com/mediacom/rodos/thecity.html
Step-by-step sightseeing walks through the old city, the even older city and the modern town.

Iceland

Icelandic Tourist Board   http://www.icetourist.is
Touted as an island of contrasts, with the midnight sun and its Viking history. This official tourist website incorporates the practical (Icelandic yellow pages) with the bizarre.

Next Door To Nature   http://www.rvk.is
Reykjavik is the European city of culture for the year 2000. So once you've looked at the accommodation and sightseeing guides here, make sure you absorb the in-depth arts and culture tour.

Ireland

Access Ireland   http://www.visunet.ie/aulysses.htm
These guys claim to be the smartest link to all things Irish, and after visiting the virtual pub for a bit of blarney we wouldn't disagree. The cultural and accommodation guides are map-led and comprehensive.

Cork City   http://www.aardvark.ie/cork
Superbly simple site with visitor information and local government

directories alongside a calendar of events and a brief history of the city itself.

This Week In Galway http://www.wombat.ie/galwayguide

Not actually updated weekly, but we'll forgive them that. A nice site design has a scrolling navigation frame allowing easy access to all areas such as street maps, things to do and transport links.

Local Ireland: Killarney http://kerry.local.ie/killarney

9,000 years of rich heritage packed into a directory-style site complete with drop-down menu listings for ease of use.

Limerick Life http://www.limericklife.com

This website's designed by a clever dick
With so much to be found with a single click
So follow your mouse
Right out of the house
And discover the beauty of Limerick

Waterford Guide http://www.waterford-guide.com

As well as a visitor guide and live webcasts by local radio, this site has a unique section on tracing your Irish ancestry. Even if you don't think you have any.

Italy

Italy.com http://www.initaly.com/index.htm

Not the best looking of websites but like a meat feast pizza with extra anchovies, the content begs to be consumed.

Welcome to the Incredible http://www.tiac.
Town of Florence net/users/pendini

After such a trumpet-blowing introduction this text-heavy site may disappoint you. But this does mean you get to the considerable information contained about Florence a whole lot quicker.

4Milan.Com   http://www.4milan.com/city.shtml
City-centre maps and guides plus detailed information to help you
find the best restaurants and hotels in town.

Naples2000   http://tqd.advanced.org/2838/napl2000.htm
A straightforward, straight talking overview of Naples. The student
author invites guests to join in an email conversation for further
insights.

The Best of Parma   http://www.parmaitaly.com
Where the ham and cheese come from. Learn more about them
and the city of castles from this delightful directory-cum-magazine.

Pisa in Virtual Reality   http://www.webcomp.com/virtuale
An otherwise ordinary square becomes the 'Piazza dei Miracoli'
thanks to the leaning tower, the baptistery and the cathedral.
Providing you have the QuickTime plug-in for your web browser
you can see the lot in virtual reality.

All Roads Lead   http://www.geocities.
To Rome   com/Athens/Forum/2680
An enthusiastic tourist guide to Rome – with museums and
galleries, favourite restaurants, churches and shops – by someone
who clearly loves the place.

Virtual Venice   http://www.virtualvenice.com
You need to be Shockwave-equipped to get the best from this
highly interactive site. But if you have the latest in web browsers
you get to experience the real Venice, virtually.

Verona – City of Art and History   http://www.intesys.it/Tour
A site that invites you to discover Roman Verona, Venetian Verona,
Austrian Verona and Lake Garda. Nothing about the Two
Gentlemen of Verona, though.

Latvia

Virtual Latvia http://www.vernet.lv/VT
Sometimes it seems there is just too much here. If you and your browser can cope with the densely crowded information on the page, it's worth ploughing through for the wealth of detail offered.

Riga in Your Pocket http://www.inyourpocket.com/Latvia
As far as we can tell, the only online guide to the Latvian capital – and it's a good one. You could order a printed copy, but when the website's so good, why bother?

Luxembourg

Luxembourg Tourist Office http://www.luxembourg.co.uk
An impressive and varied website. Treasures include the city street map and the Luxembourg folklore section.

Luxembourg – The City http://www.luxembourg-city.lu
The official city tourist office provides an insight into the capital with this lively guide. Make sure you check out the interactive map and promenade while here.

Malta

It's Malta http://www.visitmalta.com
An ambitious site with streaming video and all the usual information. The people who run the site will deal with any unanswered questions by email. Now that's what we call a tourist service.

Monaco

Monaco Online Guide http://www.monaco.mc/monaco/index.html
A superb photo gallery is just one reason to visit Monaco Online. The sporting stuff, the history and the royalty are a few others.

Monte Carlo Online　　　　http://www.montecarloresort.com
The posh part of already posh-enough Monaco, Monte Carlo is
arguably the oldest and most exclusive resort in the world. Plus
there's the chance to lose all your worldly goods at the casino – or
perhaps break the bank.

Netherlands

Visit Holland　　　　　　　http://www.visitholland.com
As comprehensive a guide to Holland as you could hope for. In the
'off the beaten track' section you can discover where to eat fish
with famous painters and rock'n'roll in a butcher's shop.

Electronic Mainport of Rotterdam　　http://www.rotterdam.nl
No, we don't know what the website title is on about either. But
we do know that the site has great links to the tourist attractions
and infrastructure of the town.

Northern Ireland

Northern Ireland　　　　　　　　　http://www.ni-
Tourist Board　　　　　　　tourism.com/getplugin.htm
Lots of Shockwave animations here – and a vast database of travel
information for the whole of Northern Ireland.

Exploring　　　　　　　　　　　　http://www.
Belfast　　　　　interknowledge.com/northern-ireland
A guide to Belfast's points of interest. Art galleries, theatres and
pubs get separate detailed listings, while the other attractions are
simply described on this single page.

Glens of Antrim　　　　　　　http://antrim.local.ie
County Antrim, home of the Giant's Causeway, described with a
combination of evocative language and links to relevant external
websites.

Welcome to County Armagh   http://www.countyarmagh.com
As soon as this website appears on your screen you know you've hit the jackpot. Click on an interactive map of the county or select from well-categorised subsections.

The Coast of Down   http://www.coastofdown.com
Explore County Down from the viewpoint of more than 200 miles of coastline. An index bar provides quick access to an A-Z of everything from arts and crafts to zoos.

Welcome to   http://www.
County Fermanagh   countyfermanagh.com
Clickable maps, straightforward access to towns by alphabetical listing and an eye for detail covering everything from accommodation to the whereabouts of banks and sports facilities.

Tourist Net UK –   http://www.
Londonderry   touristnetuk.com/NI/LONDONDERRY
Detailed listings of accommodation, travel and transportation services, attractions and activities in County Londonderry.

Welcome to County Tyrone   http://www.countytyrone.com
All the towns in the county explored, plus refreshingly quick links to accommodation and travel indices. Terrific pub and restaurant listings with photographs, full descriptions and contact details.

Norway

Norwegian Scenery   http://www.norwegian-scenery.com
My word, there's a lot going on here. Little details like the official flag-flying days make the site very appealing.

Oslo Clickwalk   http://oslo.clickwalk.no
An intriguing way to explore Oslo using photography and maps. Click on a photo to start and then use the compass and zoom tools to start your virtual walk. Accompanying text and overview maps ensure you don't get lost and are kept informed along the way.

Poland

Poland in Sound,   **http://www.**
Noise and Pictures   **outdoor.se/artiklar/poland**
Some bloke went to Poland on holiday, and when he got back he built this eclectic website. It's an unusual and interesting way to experience the country from a traveller's perspective.

Magical Cracow   **http://www.krakow.pl/WK/EN/**
What's on, hotel guides and tourist attractions. The World Directory of Cracovians could be an interesting feature, if they ever get it finished.

Gdansk   **http://www.polandtour.org/cities/gdansk.html**
A simple yet effective guide to the tri-city complex of Gdansk. Discover the old town, read up on its history, check out the suburbs and take a peek at the available day trips.

Virtual Tour   **http://www.geocities.**
of Warsaw   **com/Heartland/9413/Tour.htm**
Maps, photos and brief but descriptive writing are the hallmarks of this personal guide to Warsaw. As well as the tourist information there's an interesting local history section for good measure.

Portugal

Tourism   **http://www.**
Portugal   **portugal.org/tourism/tourism.html**
Where the Atlantic meets Europe. Portugal's art, tradition and culture exposed by the Ministry of Economy.

Algarve Life   **http://www.algarve-life.com**
The 'Algarvian in 2 minutes' crash course sets you up with local knowledge before reading what a local journalist thinks about the Algarve. There's also video footage and a business guide.

The Azores Islands http://www.geocities.com/
Web Pages TheTropics/2140/azores.html
Amazingly detailed website covering the nine islands that make up the Azores archipelago. Includes the words (in English and Portuguese) to the national anthem and satellite pictures of the islands from NASA.

About http://gothere.
Lisbon gformula.com/eng/gothere.A21FE81.run
No matter what you need to know about Lisbon, this guide can help. Nice touches include opening times for banks, shops and museums.

Madeira Web http://www.madeira-web.com/PagesUK
Superb design meets good content in this award-winning site. A live webcam, panoramic movies, recommended hotels and resorts, plus a new photo of island life every day.

Romania

Romanian Travel Guide http://www.rotravel.com
Everything for the discerning traveller to the land of the gypsies. A calendar of events, a database of hotels and even a lively discussion forum.

Travelling to Bucharest http://bucharest.com/bol/travelf.html
An all-in-one resource site for Romania's capital. From the one location you can check on currency exchange rates, the weather, the local lingo and recommended hotels.

Former Soviet Union

Russia Tourism Pages http://russia-tourism.com
The new autonomous regions of the former USSR exposed for the traveller. A vast array of links available that include such diverse subjects as children, visas, money and language – and a built-in search engine to help you make sense of it all.

Moscow Guide   http://www.moscow-guide.ru

Hotel and travel guides, cultural and historical links.

Moscow Life   http://solar.rtd.utk.edu/~asebrant/life/ml.html

If you prefer your tourist guide absolutely free of political comment then try Moscow Life. Now in its fifth year, what you get is a wonderful insight into the city through the eyes of a Muscovite.

Welcome to Altai   http://arw.dcn-asu.ru

An overview of the autonomous republic of Altai and links to a series of personal pages add further local colour.

Chechen Republic Online   http://www.amina.com

A website whose content is monitored by the government of the troubled Chechen Republic. The maps, photography and cultural overviews are interesting, even if travel to Chechnya looks tricky, to say the least.

Dagestan

A Land Woven   http://www.
From Legends   geocities.com/CollegePark/Union/6282

A Dagestani abroad brings this delightful online tour, complete with useful links to other sites such as the state dance company and the Dagestani government.

Evenki

The Unofficial Evenki   http://www.spri.cam.ac.uk/
Home Page   people/jeoh2/2evenki.htm

A particularly useful and totally unofficial guide to this region. We liked the flags after the links that show which languages they are written in, and which saved many a wasted journey.

Karelia

Tourist Sights   http://www.
of Karelia   gov.karelia.ru/gov/info/tourism_e.html

Part of a rather austere government site with plenty of information about political bodies. But still good.

Tatarstan

Tatarstan on the Internet http://www.kcn.ru/tat_en
One for the determined traveller. An in-depth tour of the republic plus a look at the capital city, Kazan.

Tuva

Tuvan Photo Gallery http://www.cbc.umn.edu/~sklar/tpics.html
Sparse comments and variable photographs from a 1995 tourist trip to Tuva are just about the only travel resources available for this obscure region.

Udmurtia

Udmurtia Republic Directory http://www.udm.ru
Broken links and inconsistent information, but this is one of the few online links into Udmurtia.

Scotland

Scotland Travel Guide http://www.destination-scotland.com
Nice search facility brings near-instant results when you type a town or hotel name. If you want answers to specific questions then 'Ask Hamish' on an online form and he'll email the answers back to you.

The Aberdeen Advantage http://www.aberdeen.net.uk/tourism/links.cfm
Pointers to websites that cover just about every aspect of tourism in and around Aberdeen.

Dumfries.Net http://www.dumfries.net
A well-indexed selection of site reviews in an efficiently designed site.

Dundee – City of Discovery http://www.dundeecity.gov.uk
The city council provides this excellent introduction to Dundee. Local history archives and a city-centre map accompany the exhaustive tourism pages.

Edinburgh First City http://www.firstcity.force9.co.uk
The dull colour scheme can get irksome after a while, but don't let that put you off an otherwise superbly implemented guide to Edinburgh.

Virtual Glasgow City Guide http://www.virtualglasgow.com
Straightforward design with a webcam, tourist information and a newsgroup to chat to the locals.

Inverness – Capital of http://www.scotland-
the Highlands inverness.co.uk
Joanne Mackenzie-Winters shows just what can be achieved with a lot of passion for a region. The website covers all the surrounding sights including Loch Ness.

John O'Groats Ferries http://www.jogferry.co.uk
As well as timetables and ferry information there are loads of links to tour guides and accommodation in the area.

Perthshire Tourist Board http://www.perthshire.co.uk
At the heart of Scotland, Perthshire covers 2,000 square miles of countryside and bustling towns alike. This official tourist board site has a useful travel tips section covering disabled facilities, motoring and accommodation.

Shetland Islands Tourism http://www.shetland-tourism.co.uk
How to get there and where to stay, plus inter-island ferries and flights. Check out the Shetland Experience section for a virtual taste of the islands.

Slovakia

Our Slovakia   http://www.our-slovakia.com
The shopping, the food, the people, the places – as seen by the locals.

Bratislava City Guide   http://www.bratislava.com
The capital of Slovakia since 1993 is explored in statistical detail here.

Slovenia

National Tourist   http://www.ntz-
Association   nta.si/Ang_menu.htm
This official website is sombre and rudimentary in its design, but it delivers enough tourist information to merit its place here.

Ljubljana   http://www.ijs.si/slo/ljubljana
One of the smallest European capitals, with just 280,000 inhabitants. A site packed with information and an interactive map of the city centre.

Spain

All About Spain   http://www.red2000.com/spain
Beyond the vibrant colours lies a real beauty of a travel information site. The 'Traveller's A-Z' is of particular interest, with its very comprehensive index of links.

SpainTour –   http://www.
Barcelona   spaintour.com/barcelona.html
A colourful guide to the city and its people, with an evocative description of the famous Ramblas.

Benidorm Web Guide   http://www.athenea.com/benidorm
Well, well. Here's a Benidorm search engine, an electronic postcards facility and very complete lodging and eating guides.

Marbella: http://www.pgb.es/
The City   marbella/html/iciudad.html
A well-crafted directory guide, with an exhaustive series of maps
and an interesting news and media section.

SoftGuide   http://www.
Madrid   softguides.com/index_madrid.html
A magazine-style guide, where design is as important as content.
Whether you need a vegetarian restaurant or a hospital, it'll be
listed here.

The Sevilla Page   http://www.andalucia.com/cities/sevilla.htm
A superbly simple guide to the city by a local travel journalist. We
were strangely drawn to the 'recommended tapas bars' section.

Tenerife Convention Bureau   http://www.tenerifecb.com
An unconventional route to an island guide, but a good one
nonetheless. The island and hotel directories are of interest to all
travellers, not just those arriving on business.

Valencia: A Virtual Trip   http://www.upv.es/cv/valbegin.html
A nicely presented guide to Valencia, in English and Catalan,
covering gardens, gastronomy and more.

Sweden

The Information   http://www.
Smorgasbord   sverigeturism.se/smorgasbord
Not a single Muppet chef or boxy estate car in sight, but plenty of
tourist, cultural and practical information on the Swedish way
of life.

Welcome to Stockholm   http://www.stockholm.se/english
The official tourist guide to the city of Stockholm, with a hilariously
immodest regular newsletter feature.

Switzerland

Destination Switzerland http://www.lonelyplanet.com.au/dest/eur/swi.htm

The Lonely Planet come up trumps again with their destination guide to the home of triangular chocolate and clocks that chirp.

Welcome to Berne http://www.berntourismus.ch

The official tourist guide to the Swiss capital. Plenty of quality maps and equally high-quality information about the city and surrounding areas.

Geneva Networld http://www.geneva.ch

A fairly conventional site packed with gripping facts. Did you know there are 7,378 rooms in Geneva's 105 hotels?

Zurich Tourism http://www.zurichtourism.ch

The English language version of this site, with a 'build it yourself' city guide that lets you plan your stay by selecting sections of personal interest. If you (inexplicably) have no interest in Zurich nightlife, for example, you can exclude it from your guide.

Ukraine

http://pages.prodigy.net/euroscope/guidetoc.html

Small rural towns as well as the major tourist centres.

Vatican City

Vatican: The Holy See http://www.vatican.va

The Pope's official site includes maps and tourist guides of the city and its fabulous museums.

Wales

Welcome to Wales http://www.croeso.com

A small country with a big heart and beautiful countryside. This site has an extensive Welsh-links index, and divides its information between seaside, inland and historic areas.

Betws-y-Coed Welcomes You http://snowdonia.org.uk
Nestled in the Snowdonia National Park, Betws-y-Coed is renowned for its beauty. And the site is beautiful too.

Tour Cardiff http://www.tigerbay.com/newcity
Jump straight to the A-Z subject index if you are in a hurry, or take a leisurely ramble around the city using the clickable interactive map.

Westys Unofficial Guide http://www.
To Llandudno llandudno.cwc.net
A typical Welsh seaside resort is revealed in this personal home-page tribute to the town. Listing of links to other sites and resources is the order of the day here.

Llanfair http://llanfairpwllgwyngyllg
PG ogerychwyrndrobwllllantysiliogogogoch.co.uk
This guide to the town of Llanfairpwllgwyngyllgogerychwyrndrob wllllantysiliogogogoch holds the honour of the longest URL on the web as well as the longest place name in Britain. If you have the patience to type it into your browser, there's a hotel and restaurant guide as well as a detailed history.

Virtual Portmeirion http://www.virtualportmeirion.com
Known for its pottery and as the spooky location for the cult TV series The Prisoner, Portmeirion is an enchanting place. The website takes you inside this private village, built as a folly by the eccentric architect Sir Clough Williams-Ellis.

City of http://www.swansea-
Swansea gower.demon.co.uk/109swan.htm
A brief but adequate guide to the city, with the all-important

city car park directory and a programme of events at the Grand Theatre.

MIDDLE EAST

Brunei

Brunei Darussalam Homepage   http://www.brunet.bn
Stunning images, a news ticker and tourist attractions hardly scratch the surface of this Java-heavy, comprehensive site.

Iran

Iran Online   http://www.iranonline.com
You really can dip into Iranian culture here with the help of chat forums. A fact file that stretches from architecture to proverbs helps you bridge any Persian gulf.

Iraq

Arab Net: Iraq   http://www.arab.net/iraq/iraq_contents.html
A very complete tour guide of this country, with plenty about its fascinating and long history. And the hanging gardens of Babylon.

Israel

Go Israel   http://www.goisrael.com
Often described as the land where time began, Israel is a popular tourist destination, well served by this impressive official tourist board site.

Eilat Net   http://eilat.net
A very busy site that reflects the bustling resort of Eilat. Weather reports and event guides nestle alongside transport information and both English and Hebrew chat forums.

Jerusalem Interactive   **http://www.**
Tourism Guide   **insite.co.il/jer/jer.htm**
Detailed maps, histories and general tourist information. Full of practicalities like where to rent a cellular phone.

Nazareth City Official Website **http://www.nazareth.muni.il**
This site reflects the historical and biblical importance of Jesus's hometown without sacrificing the tourist info, so hotel directories nestle alongside museum and history links.

Tel Aviv City Connection   **http://www.tel-aviv.cc**
Directory-style design crammed full of essential details. You can almost smell the felafel.

Jordan

Jordan Tourism Board   **http://www.tourism.com.jo**
A beautiful site summed up by the slogan, 'If Jordan was not, in fact, the cradle of civilisation, it was most certainly its nursery.'

Lebanon

Lebanon   **http://www.lebanon-**
Attractions   **online.com.lb/tourism/attr.html**
A small country with a big heart and a remarkable history, now at peace again and revealed in all its glory here. Some surprises in store, like the section on skiing.

Focus on   **http://focusmm.**
Lebanon: Beirut   **com.au/lebanon/beirut_1.htm**
An overview of this war-ravaged city and the progress of its reconstruction.

Tripoli City   **http://tripoli-city.org**
An interesting site that offers radio broadcasts as well as maps, photo galleries and notable quotes to illustrate the city.

Oman

Tourism Oman   http://www.oman-online.com/tourism
The Sultanate of Oman is one of the last truly untouristed destinations. All the same, this site proves they'd quite like you to pay a visit.

Palestine

Visit Palestine   http://www.visit-palestine.com/main.htm
The Ministry of Tourism & Antiquities has an uphill struggle to promote this newly autonomous region as a tourist attraction, and has opted to use glorious photography as its strategy.

Saudi Arabia

Living and Working in   http://darkwing.
Saudi Arabia   uoregon.edu/~kbatarfi/travel.html
A fascinating insight into the country and its culture, from an insider's perspective.

Syria

Ministry of Tourism   http://www.syriatourism.org
Cuisine and culture sit happily side by side on this official site. The tour pages are a wonderful mix of intriguing imagery and descriptive text.

United Arab Emirates

United Arab Emirates Home Page   http://www.emirates.org
The tradition and heritage of the seven emirates, a presidential profile, plenty of facts and figures and practical information for tourists. Oh yes, and an incredibly tiny photo gallery.

Yemen

Yemen Tourism   http://www.yemen-online.com/tourism
Make sure you take a look at the delightful 'Yemen in pictures'

image gallery. There's enough statistical information here to satisfy the most ravenous fact collector.

NORTH AMERICA

Canada

Travel   **http://www.canadatourism.**
Canada   **com/en/ctc/travel_canada**
Discover Canada with the help of a virtual tour, coast to coast. A well-designed site with a built-in search facility to speed up your visit.

Destination Calgary   **http://www.calgary.net**
One of the fastest growing cities in North America, Calgary was once just an 'oil city'. Now it's much more, as this interesting website reveals.

Discover Edmonton   **http://www.discoveredmonton.com**
Now this is what we call a professional looking website. It's almost so good that you don't need to actually visit Edmonton to feel you've been there.

Halifax Visitor Information   **http://www.halifaxinfo.com**
A wonderful site full of interesting-sounding places like Clam Harbour and Peggy's Cove. Well designed, with pop-up and drop-down menus to ease navigation.

Montreal e-Guide   **http://www.pagemontreal.qc.ca/meg**
An exhaustive electronic guide to what to do, where to go and where to stay in this lively city.

Info Niagara   **http://www.infoniagara.com**
More than just a bloody big waterfall. The many wonders of Niagara are explored on this simple but interesting site.

A Capital Century   http://www.capcan.ca/english/index.html
The official Ottowa website offers a little bit of something for just about everyone who may want to visit. The pop quizzes on the way in are tedious, but get past them and everything is tickety boo.

Quebec City Guide   http://www.telegraphe.com/introen.html
We've pinpointed the English language version of this website, but there's a French one as well if you want to be truly authentic.

Toronto.Com   http://www.toronto.com
An enormous interactive magazine dedicated to everything Toronto. The 'visitors & getaways' section is probably most relevant to the average tourist.

Discover Vancouver   http://www.discovervancouver.com
Places to go, things to do, and even online games designed to help you discover Vancouver.

City of Victoria   http://www.city.victoria.bc.ca
Incredibly detailed site, right down to parking fines and how to pay them. The virtual tours and in-depth weather reports are welcome as well.

Mexico

MexGuide   http://rtn.net.mx/mexguide
A straightforward guide to Mexico for the would-be visitor. Beaches and architecture are given equal importance and the old and new cities of Mexico likewise.

A Guide to Acapulco   http://acapulco.com
You won't be going loco down in Acapulco if you do your homework here before you leave.

Complete Cabo Guide   http://www.caboland.com
Plenty of information here, but the messy design can be distracting. Still, it is worth digging around for the travel gems dotted around the site.

Welcome to Cancun http://cancun.yucatanweb.com/Cancun
A refreshingly down-to-earth guide to one of the Mayan Riviera's best-known tourist traps. The site uses a folders-and-files metaphor for navigation that will be recognisable to all computer users.

Cozumel Fan Club http://www.sfn.saskatoon.sk.ca/~af943
This splendid site brings a little bit of Mexico they would like you to see more of. Updated very regularly by a passionate publisher.

City of http://www.mexconnect.
Festivals com/mex_/guadalajara/guadalajara.html
Home of the famous Mariachi Festival, Guadalajara also boasts this spicy Mexican-flavoured website.

Travel to Mazatlan http://www.maztravel.com
Visit the website, cut out the coupons (don't ask us how), and get free drinks when you holiday in Mazatlan.

Mexico City Life http://mexicocitylife.com
A hotel, restaurant and shopping guide combined with a directory of attractions and a welcome from the Secretary of Tourism. Somehow it manages to be much more interesting than it sounds.

Puerto Vallarta's http://www.
Official Website puertovallarta.net
Where Mexico comes to life, and the mayor provides a personal welcome, virtually speaking of course.

San Jose http://www.bajaexpo.
Del Cabo com/cities/sanjose.htm
The gateway to the Los Cabos Corridor, with great satellite photography.

Tijuana Mexico http://www.sdro.com/tj.htm
A comprehensive guide to this famous border town, with the bazaars, shopping malls and pest-control centres.

US Travel Guide   http://www.usatourist.com
A directory site full of cool places to go and interesting things to do. The 'Hot Tips' section contains practical advice on safety, visas, driving and shopping.

Unforgettable Alabama   http://www.touralabama.org
The Alabama Bureau of Tourism and Travel present their introduction to the state. What to do, where to stay and, for some reason, where to play golf.

Alaska Tourism and   http://www.
Travel Guide   alaskanet.com/Tourism
A virtual tour of the last frontier. Excellent transport links, including taxi services and boat charters.

Arizona Guide   http://www.arizonaguide.com
Home to the eighth wonder of the world, the Grand Canyon, and a helluva lot more besides. High points include the instant access weather forecasts and a tour of Arizona ghost towns.

Explore Arkansas   http://www.arkansas.com
An interactive tour planner and a section just for kids make this tour guide stand out from the crowd.

California Travel & Tourism   http://gocalif.ca.gov
Maps, lodgings, destinations and, of course, the movie tour of California. A good search facility and translations into five languages round off a good package.

Colorado Com   http://www.colorado.com
Detailed regional information provided by way of a series of impressive maps.

Connecticut Tourism   http://www.tourism.state.ct.us
The official tourism guide to the 'state of surprises'. No surprises here though – just the usual array of traveller stuff.

Delaware Visitors   http://visitors.delawareonline.com
Attractions, events, state parks, lodging and history. Plus excellent maps of the entire state.

See Florida   http://www.see-florida.com
Select your Florida region from the drop-down list and soak up the tourist information that is revealed.

Georgia on my Mind   http://www.gomm.com
History, trails, culture and more all dished up with traditional southern hospitality.

Hawaii Visitors   http://www.
Guide   maui.net/~leodio/higuide.html
A superb guide to Hawaii from a couple of residents who used to be tourists themselves.

Discover Idaho   http://www.visitid.org
Another comprehensive information site with the visitor in mind. A 'river flow' section will satisfy all water babies.

Travel Illinois   http://www.welcometraveler.com
An interactive map is your gateway to this online tour of Illinois with a nice homely feel to it all.

Visit Indiananet   http://www.visitindiana.net
As well as the expected info, there's a whole section on 'Famous Hoosiers' – that's people from Indiana to you and me.

Kansas Department of   http://www.kansascommerce.com/
Commerce and Housing   0400travel.html
KATIE (Kansas Area Travel Ideas and Events), the online travel planner, is at the heart of this intriguing guide full of long acronyms.

The Great Kentucky   http://www.
Getaway Guide   state.ky.us/tour/tour.htm
From the bluegrass heartlands to the scenic wonderlands, all of Kentucky is here in glorious detail.

Louisiana Travel   http://www.louisianatravel.com
Find out about the 'fall festivals', which celebrate everything and anything – from shrimps to gasoline.

Visit Maine   http://www.visitmaine.com
A 365-day calendar of events, lodging directory, a region-by-region tourist guide and more.

Welcome to Maryland   http://www.mdisfun.org
'So many things to do, so close together' – that's the message here, as well as an unhealthy interest in golf.

Welcome to Massachusetts   http://www.mass-vacation.com
Want to eat a lobster like a native? Even if you don't, they cover other more practical tourist stuff here as well.

Yes Michigan   http://www.yesmichigan.com/cities
Another state that seems to have a high golf-course-to-everything-else ratio. Discover them all here.

Explore Minnesota   http://www.exploreminnesota.com
Special features on different regions, a fishing field guide, and even email access to 'Travel Counsellors' should you need one.

The South's Warmest Welcome   http://www.
to Mississippi   visitmississippi.org
Hunting, fishing, gambling and other traditional local pastimes are covered here. A compact and nicely designed site that still manages to pack in more information than at first seems possible.

The Official Show Me   http://www.
Missouri Website   show-me-missouri.com/tourism.html-ssi
A bit of a grey website, but you can't knock the content, which is comprehensive and interesting.

Montana's Official Travel Guide   http://travel.mt.gov
The official state travel and adventure guide that manages to

capture the essence of a 147,000-square-mile state on your 15" monitor quite well.

Visit Nebraska http://www.visitnebraska.org

You are invited to explore the state by exploring the site. Be sure to check out Omaha's historic Old Market district while you are here.

The Complete http://www.
Nevada Traveller nevadaweb.com/cnt

A big state – and a big site as well. This manages to pack in everything from cowboy country to Las Vegas territory with all the in-betweens.

New Hampshire – http://www.
The Road Less Travelled visitnh.gov

Whether it's the great outdoors that interests you or shopping malls and tourist attractions, you'll find the details here. A good-looking site that's easy to navigate and heavy on content.

Friendly New Jersey http://www.geocities.com/~orgacki

A personal and friendly guide to New Jersey from Anka and Adam. Er, and Adam's cat, 'PC'.

New Mexico Department of http://www.
Tourism newmexico.org

Surf down Route 66 and discover the land that is New Mexico. The full-colour state highway map is a useful addition, and the drop-down menus make navigation a breeze.

This Is New York State! http://iloveny.state.ny.us

We'll forgive them for still pushing the 'I ♥ New York' stuff, but only just. Plenty for new visitors and old NY hands alike.

Visit North Carolina http://www.visitnc.com

Nothing could be finer, than to be in Carolina, in a website. Or something like that.

Rough Guide to North Dakota http://travel.roughguides.com/content/1036/

The Rough Guides do their thing with North Dakota, with the usual good results.

Oklahoma Native America http://www.travelok.com

What we can only describe as a magical tour of the 'Native America', Oklahoma. Superb imagery and an evocative atmosphere coupled with informative content.

Ohio Tourism http://www.ohiotourism.com

Ohio hotspots, Hocking Hills to Lake Erie Islands, and not forgetting Amish country. A good search engine and online hotel reservations stake this site out from the others.

Travel Oregon http://www.traveloregon.com

Whether you want to go 'into the outdoors' or discover what is 'uniquely Oregon', this is a good starting point.

Welcome to Pennsylvania http://www.visit.state.pa.us

Cities, mountains and forests nestling with Pirates, Steelers and Penguins.

The Most Complete Guide To Rhode Island http://www.ritourism.com

A lovely site. Anecdotes about the King of Rhode Island mix with streaming video of Narragansett Beach.

South Carolina http://www.sccsi.com/sc

The 'Smiling Face, Beautiful Places' mentality might make you want to retch, but the information content is beyond reproach.

South Dakota Department of Tourism http://www.state.sd.us./tourism

Probably best known for Mount Rushmore, South Dakota is also the Sioux Nation. Email postcards and a webcam feature on this well-presented website.

Tennweb Tourism   http://www.tennweb.com/tourism

From Cherokee hunting to tourism in Memphis, Tennessee has it all. The Tennweb tourism pages are a useful starting point to find out more about the diversity of the state.

Travel Tex   http://www.traveltex.com

Tours of Texas, postcards, history, a CD-ROM to order, and even a screensaver to download. The multiple drop-down menus approach to navigation makes finding the right information simple.

Discover Utah   http://www.infowest.com/Utah

Discover life, discover Utah, discover dinosaur land, Salt Lake country and the golden spike empire. You're going to have to visit the site to find out what that all meant.

Utah Adventure Travel   http://www.utah.com

National parks, ski resorts, mountain biking, rafting and golfing – if it happens in Utah you can read about it here.

Visit New England   http://www.visit-vermont.com

The Green Mountain State is well served by this site. Don't miss the 'leaf peeping' guide to foliage colour in the different seasons.

Virginia Life   http://www.virginia-life.com

An extremely in-depth look at Virginia, including nightlife, sports resources, the military and something for the kids. The directory-style suits such an information-packed site.

Visit Washington DC   http://www.dchomepage.net

Not the prettiest of websites, but that doesn't matter if the content is good and fortunately it is. Maps abound, including Metro guides, schedules and fares. A good overview of the USA's capital.

Washington State Tourism Home Pages   http://www.tourism.wa.gov

A link to Washington DC if you have lost your way and a plea to stay and savour the flavour of Washington State instead. We'd stay; it's worth it.

West Virginia – http://www.
Wild and Wonderful state.wv.us/tourism

Let the country roads take you home, mountain momma. Or maybe take the white water rafting route instead. An eclectic collection of tourist information.

Wyoming Tourism http://www.
Information state.wy.us/state/tourism/tourism.html

You might want to avoid the 632Kb audio file download from the governor, but don't miss the rest of an otherwise excellent site.

OCEANIA

American Samoa

Amerika http://www.ipacific.com/
Samoa samoa/samoa.html

Draw a triangle between Hawaii, New Zealand and Tahiti and bang in the middle you'll find American Samoa. This site contains everything from a language tutor to a look at traditional Samoan weddings.

Australia

The Aussie Traveller http://www.wilmap.com.au

Thousands of maps and hundreds of photos. A rather busy interface using too many frames, but worth putting up with for the magnificent content.

Australia's National http://www.
Capital canberratourism.com.au

Canberra, that is. A rather daunting site at first glance, when you're confronted with row upon row of drop-down menu boxes.

However, once you get over the initial shock, this fussy interface actually makes the site easy to navigate.

Discover the ACT   http://www.about-australia.com

A non-fussy website about the Australian Capital Territory (that's the area around Canberra) that covers health and education along with the usual travel tips, maps and tour guides.

Sapphire Coast Tourism   http://www.sapphirecoast.com.au

Concentrates on the south coast region of New South Wales. Travel guides for all the major resorts, plus details of the enchanting Eden Whale Festival.

Australian Northern Territory   http://www.
Tourist Web   nttc.com.au

All the usual accommodation and sightseeing stuff you'd expect from an official tourist board site. The 'Itinerary Ideas' section, with its well-fleshed-out tour plans, is particularly useful.

Destination   http://www.queensland-
Queensland   holidays.com.au

An excellent overview of the most popular holiday territory in Australia. A good search facility, lots of maps and an online reservation facility – if you like what you see so much, you'll want to book a holiday there and then.

SouthAustralia.Com   http://www.kern.
                                        com.au/users/southaustralia

A truly massive site with links to hosted and external websites for the business and leisure travellers.

Web Weavers Tasmania   http://www.wwt.com.au

Explore Tasmania using 'click-thru' maps. Select a regional map, click on a destination and get transported to an information guide.

Tourism Victoria   http://www.tourism.vic.gov.au

Victoria is Australia's most compact mainland state. This website looks small on the outside but is huge inside. Prepare to be amazed as you delve into ever more detailed pages.

Western Australia   **http://www.**
Tourism Commission   **westernaustralia.net**
A superb site with some innovative ideas, like the 'personal travel folder' that lets you file information as you browse by clicking on a folder icon. When you are finished you can go back to your personal folder and read at your leisure or print out for reference.

Cook Islands

http://www.cook-islands.com
Beautiful, atmospheric and practical. Flight schedules, restaurant guides and good places to shop.

Easter Island

Easter Island Home Page   **http://www.netaxs.com/~trance**
Famous for the massive carved statues, but there's much more to Easter Island, as this unofficial guide reveals.

Federated States of Micronesia

FSM Visitors Board   **http://www.visit-fsm.org**
OK, we had never heard of Yap, Chuuk, Pohnpei and Kosrae either. But after browsing this beautifully presented tour of the islands we may just add them on to our holiday wish list.

Fiji

Fiji Islands Information Centre   **http://www.internetfiji.com**
Fiji was the first country to enter the third millennium and, boy, do they want to let you know about it. There's also plenty of more useful tourism information here, though.

French Polynesia

Chris Davis's   http://www.cd-
French Polynesia   enterprises.com/french_polynesia
One man's mission to uncover the beauty of this island group to a
wider audience. He accomplishes this with a simple yet effective
overview of the islands.

Guam

The Official Guam USA Website   http://ns.gov.gu
The nature photography on this site is breathtaking. The rest of it is
packed with useful official tourist information.

Kiribati

Kiribati, Tarawa   http://www.hideawayholidays.com.
and Christmas Island   au/trw_.htm
An independent republic, comprising the Gilbert, Phoenix and
Line islands. If relics of World War II are your thing, you'll like
Kiribati.

Marshall Islands

Marshall Islands   http://www.
Internet Guide   rmiembassyus.org
Halfway between Hawaii and Australia, the Republic of the
Marshall Islands may be small, but it's wondrous. This site brings
you government statistics, tourist information and links to other
related sites.

Nauru

Nations of the   http://www.tbc.gov.bc.ca/
Commonwealth: Nauru   cwgames/country/Nauru/nauru.html
A coral atoll and one of the smallest republics in the world. A popu-

lation of less than 10,000 and a website that belies its equally small proportions to pack an informational punch.

New Caledonia

The Biggest Lagoon in the World   **http://www.new-caledonia.com**

Island facts, activities, transportation, food and shopping facilities are all here.

New Zealand

Country Digest: New Zealand   **http://newpaper.asia1.com.sg/journey/travel/nz/nz.html**

The 'land of the long white cloud' explored in depth, region by region. A 'fast facts' section covers all the vital tourist stuff like visas, customs and currency, and the 'odds and ends' section has an amusing guide to local lingo to keep you occupied.

Wellington NZ.Com   **http://www.wellingtonnz.com**

A useful and in-depth overview of New Zealand's capital city – what to see, when to go and how to get there. Detailed maps of the city centre and the central business district are also provided.

Tourism BOP   **http://www.visitplenty.co.nz**

No matter how you plan to visit the Bay of Plenty, be it backpacking or living it up in five-star-hotel luxury, this official site points the way with plenty of accommodation, activity and cultural links.

Christchurch Tour   **http://www.cae.canterbury.ac.nz/chchtour.htm**

Beautifully simple in presentation yet comprehensive in its content. All the statistical information and website links you could ask for, wrapped up in a tidy and easy-to-browse package.

Northern Mariana Islands

Commonwealth of the http://www.
Northern Mariana Islands Home Page saipan.com

Welcome or, if you prefer, 'Hafa Adai' to the Mariana Visitors Authority website. Covers everything from the geography to the TV station.

Palau

Palau – Adventure in Paradise http://www.visit-palau.com

A 400-mile-long archipelago, home to the stunning Rock Islands, and the number one underwater wonder of the world. A no-frills, quick-loading site that does a better tourist information job than many of the bigger and flashier sites we've seen.

Papua New Guinea

Paradise Live http://www.tiare.net.pg/tpa

Plenty of natural history coverage here to go with the tourist essentials. A good-looking, sensibly designed site.

Solomon Islands

http://www.geocities.com/RainForest/4665

One guy and his camera on a sojourn in the Solomon Islands truly bring a feel for the place into your PC.

Tahiti

Tahiti.com http://www.tahiti.com

This guide is designed by a Tahitian, and the local style and knowledge shines through. Plenty of information here, from consulates and currency through to local news and a yellow pages of Tahiti businesses.

Tonga

Tonga Online　　　　　　　**http://www.tongaonline.com**

The usual tourist-oriented information for the prospective visitor. However, this site also links to the pages of Tongan artists, writers and scholars for added local value.

Tuvalu

CIA Factbook:　　　　　　**http://www.odci.gov/**
Tuvalu　　　　　　**cia/publications/factbook/tv.html**

An island group on nine coral atolls, whose people apparently have a life expectancy of precisely 63.88 years.

Vanuatu

Vanuatu　　　　　　　　**http://www.**
An Introduction　　　　**clark.net/pub/kiaman/vanuatu**

Described as 'a small place in the South Pacific', this site is a triumph of a singular passion for the island.

Western Samoa

Western　　　　　　　　**http://www.**
Samoa　　　　**merriewood.com/pacific/wsamoa1.html**

A country revealed through the lens of a regular visitor who obviously loves the place. But there's more than evocative images here, there's superbly crafted textual descriptions of his travels as well.

Try These Newsgroups

rec.travel.africa
For the armchair adventurer.

rec.travel.asia
Oriental express conversations.

rec.travel.australia+nz
Usenet down under.

rec.travel.caribbean
Laid back tropical chat.

rec.travel.europe
The true European community.

rec.travel.latin-america
Ay Caramba!

rec.travel.usa-canada
Freedom of speech personified.

5//ACTIVITY HOLIDAYS

Slowly burning away skin cells on a sunny beach somewhere is not everyone's idea of the perfect holiday. With market research suggesting that the 'average' Internet user is a twenty- or thirty-something professional with money to burn and five weeks' paid holiday a year, it should come as no surprise that the web is an adventure and activity holiday playground.

If you're sporty, choose from skiing and snowboarding in high, cold places to wreck diving in warm, wet ones. Thinking of something less energetic? How about horse riding in the Himalayas or hill-walking in the Scottish Highlands? And if you have a relaxing hobby like bird watching, fishing or photography, there's no better place to research your travel options.

Any holiday is a leap into the unknown, but the Internet does its best to show you what you'll be letting yourself in for, with detailed information, photographs and the occasional video. But above all else you can find accounts written by folk who have been there and done it. If you can't find a website where a particular activity is being discussed then turn to the Internet's discussion forums, the newsgroups. Ask questions in the right newsgroup and ye shall receive answers.

Here's just a few activity and adventure ideas to get you started. If your particular interest isn't covered here, a simple search should dig up the information you need.

//ADDRESS BOOK

Starting Points

Adventure and Speciality   http://www.travelon.com/
Travel Trip Finder   adventure
An excellent, fast, effective adventure-holiday finder. Select an activity and let the search engine find the relevant trips for you. Add a destination, departure month or budget and the list of available holidays is filtered down to your requirements.

National Parks   http://www.gorp.com/gorp/resource/
Around The World   US_National_Park/intlpark.htm
Essential for fans of unspoilt, protected wildernesses. As vast and interesting as the parks themselves.

Assorted Adventures

Above All Travel   http://www.aboveall.com
African safaris, tropical scuba diving, expeditions in Antarctica and other unusual adventure holidays feature on this intriguing site.

Adventure Quest   http://www.adventurequest.com
A travel agency offering holidays with a difference, like a gourmet bicycle tour, dog sledding and cave exploration.

Adventure Online   http://www.adventureonline.com
An online magazine that lets you join an expedition, virtually at least, to get the feel of the real thing.

Adventure Sports   http://www.
Outdoors Guide   serioussports.com
Unusual holidays for unusual people. Hang gliding, rock climbing, white water rafting and Llama trekking.

Adventure Travel http://www.
Photos mindspring.com/~jrolls/cv.html
Pictorial travelogues of cycling in Vietnam, New Zealand and Australia's Continental Divide – and kayaking in Baja.

Adventure Travel Society http://www.adventuretravel.com
Explore and understand the world, that's the message here – along with 'adventures await you', of course.

Adventure Women http://www.rainbowadventures.com
Boys keep out. Adventure holidays exclusively for women over the age of 30.

America's Best Online http://www.
National Parks americasbestonline.com
A gateway to the websites of some of the best-known parks in the USA, including Acadia, Smoky Mountain and Yellowstone.

Australia's National Parks http://www.atn.com.au
A tourism guide to the National Parks of Australia, including Kata Tjuta National Park, home to Ayers Rock.

Boojum Expeditions http://www.boojumx.com
Billed as 'uncommon adventures since 1984', this company specialises in riding, trekking or paddling in remote regions.

Cinnamon Adventure http://www.activehols.co.uk
British activity holidays, from driving military vehicles in Wales to surfing in Cornwall. Plenty of other options to set the pulse racing as well.

Desert USA http://www.desertusa.com
An online travel and adventure guide to the desert country of the American Southwest.

Earth Wise Journeys http://www.teleport.com/~earthwyz
Old hippies and eco-warriors will love the planet-friendly travel ideas here.

Ecotravel Centre http://www.ecotour.org
Vital information on travel that benefits both conservation and community.

Ecotourism Explorer http://www.ecotourism.org
Various ways to visit exotic places without damaging the planet.

Eldertreks http://www.eldertreks.com
Not a forum for Captain Kirk, Mr Spock and Scottie, but an adventure travel company for senior citizens looking for a holiday with a difference.

eTravel http://www.etravel.org
Want some adventure with your holiday? Then eTravel is a good starting point. Full of helpful advice from old hands and young lions.

Exodus http://www.exodustravels.co.uk
Overland, biking, walking or discovery – this travel company does the lot and has a very nice picture on the home page for good measure.

Explore Magazine http://www.exploremag.com/core.html
Skiing, hiking and more for the outdoor adventure enthusiast.

Explorers Club http://www.explorers.org
For 95 years the world-centre for exploration, it says here. And this professional explorers club is now on the web.

Get Lost http://www.itsnet.com/home/getlost
Stories, resources and all-round information on adventure/sports holidays.

Himalayan Travel http://www.gorp.com:80/himtravel.htm
Treks, tours, cycling, safaris and expeditions – all comers are catered for.

InfoHub   http://www.infohub.com
An odd name, but a useful service. InfoHub is a speciality travel guide for those into adventure and sports vacations.

Llama Trekking   http://www.
in Chile   torresuiza.com/llamas.htm
You want an unusual adventure holiday? You want Llama trekking in Chile, you do.

Malaysia's National Parks   http://www.interknowledge.
and Preserves   com/malaysia/nationalparks.htm
The world's oldest rainforest, with 130 million years of history behind it.

Mountain Zone   http://www.mountainzone.com
Get high on snowboarding, biking, hiking and skiing.

National Parks of Korea   http://www.npa.or.kr
Done Big Sur, Kakadu and the African veldt? Why not check out the wild spaces of Korea?

Nepal Network   http://www.visitnepal.com
Nepal is one of the world's great adventure destinations. It's all here, including trekking, rafting, safari, and even a search for the Yeti.

Old West Dude Ranch   http://www.gorp.com/oldwest
Live and work like a cowboy (or girl) for a week or two. Yee ha!

Our Trip   http://www.ourtrip.com
One couple's fascinating journey around the world. They started in 1998 travelling across the USA in a camper van, and the last report was from Cambodia – sans van.

RanchWeb   http://www.ranchweb.com
A gateway to holidays on dude ranches, cattle ranches, and the not-quite-so-authentically cowboy-sounding fly-fishing ranches.

Roller Coaster Database **http://roller.coaster.net**
If you want the ultimate thrill on wheels in America, try this list of more than 500 roller coasters to ride.

Why not test your 'adventure IQ' at http://www.mtsobek.com/test.htm. Actually it's just a way of discovering some of the adventure tours this company organises, but it is fun.

Third World Traveller **http://www.thirdworldtraveler.com**
Covering all aspects of travel to and within the third world, from basic information to health concerns and human rights issues.

Wild Dog Adventure **http://www.wild-dog.com**
If you want to go heli-skiing in British Columbia or mountain biking in the remote Peruvian countryside then Wild Dog will do their best to accommodate you.

Birdwatching

Avestravel **http://www.angelfire.com/biz/Avestravel**
Customised birding tours of Ecuador, offering bed and breakfast accommodation and the opportunity to spot the cock of the rock and fiery throated fruit eater.

Birdwatching in **http://www.birdwatching-**
Australia **australia.com**
Basic design, but full of information about twitching down under.

Canadian Wild Birdwatching **http://www.**
Adventures **canadawildbirdwatching.com**
Home of the bald eagle and great white pelican. Enough details of the holidays and the birds to satisfy any birdwatcher.

Eagle Eye Tours **http://www.eagle-eye.com**
A stunning range of birdwatching tours covering most of the

globe. Biographies of team leaders and tour reports are excellent additions.

Grus Expeditions   http://www.grus.com
And now for something completely different. Tours exploring the bird wildlife of the Russian Far East. Check the onsite map to get your bearings.

Kingfisher Tours   http://www.kthk.com.hk
An impressive site, with a search engine covering the threatened and endemic species of Hong Kong, China, Tibet and Taiwan – where they organise birdwatching tours.

Steeles Tavern Manor   http://www.symweb.com/steelestavern
A country bed and breakfast establishment complete with two-person jacuzzis and birdwatching in the shadows of the Blue Ridge Mountains of Virginia.

Wings Birdwatching Tours   http://www.widdl.com/wings
Twenty-seven years in the business of arranging small-group bird watching tours around the world. The website shows their experience, with search facilities to find tours, locations or bird species.

Canal Boating

Britain Afloat   http://www.britain-afloat.com
Be it a canal boat or a narrow boat – you'll discover the difference here – Britain Afloat has the website to unlock the secrets of holidaying on Britain's waterways.

Canalia   http://www.canalia.com
Colourful and in keeping with the canal theme. This website is a treasure trove of canal information and guides to floating holidays.

Drifters Leisure   http://www.drifters.co.uk
If your idea of the perfect self-drive holiday is on a canal rather

than a motorway then you'll love this. An information-heavy website with links to boats, destinations and holidays.

European Waterways　　http://www.europeanwaterways.com
A website from the owners and operators of canal and river cruising companies in England, France, Holland and Ireland. Comprehensive and easy to use.

H20　　　　　　　　　http://www.barginginfrance.com
450 self-drive houseboats for rent in France. Plus, for the truly lazy, hotel-barge cruises or cheaper bed and breakfast barges.

Canoeing and Kayaking

Adventure Whitewater　http://www.adventure-whitewater.com
For the daredevil traveller, fast-paced holidays on fast-flowing rivers in fast-moving canoes through Nepal, Bhutan and New Zealand.

Alaska Kayak Tours　　　　http://www.alaska.net/~nova
A tour operator offering guided sea kayaking day trips and white water adventure on six of Alaska's rivers.

Altue Active Travel　　　http://www.altueseakayak.co.cl
If you fancy a different kayak adventure, why not try sea kayaking in the Andean Fjords of northern Patagonia?

Endless River　　　　　　　　　http://www.
Adventures　　　　　　endlessriveradventures.com
White water rafting and kayak instruction on North Carolina's Nantahala River in the Smokey Mountains. The speedy website also has details of river trips to Costa Rica and Ecuador.

Water　　　　　　　　　　http://www.gorp.
Trails　　　　　com/gorp/activity/paddling/us_trail.htm
A beautiful guide to the paddling paths of America by someone who has done them in a canoe.

WaterWays   http://members.mint.net/rwirth/waterways
The paddle trip exchange website lists descriptions of fresh- and saltwater paddle trips in the US – with photos, maps, safety tips and mileage charts.

Whitewater Rafting Adventure   http://www.oars.com
Most of us would rather be on a fast-moving river than in it. Plenty of suggestions here on how and where to do it.

Wilderness Spirit   http://www.escape.ca/~wspirit
A clean and crisp design complements the tours on offer. Online booking available for guided canoe trips to Canadian subarctic regions.

Climbing

America's Roof   http://www.americasroof.com
An in-depth guide to the high spots of the USA, for mountain lovers everywhere.

Big Wall   http://www.primenet.com/~midds
How to spend days and nights on the side of the biggest, sheerest rock faces in the world.

ClimbOnline   http://www.climbonline.com
A climbing database, chat area and environmental issues.

High Places   http://www.highplaces.co.uk
Informal treks, hikes, climbs, tours and ski holidays to high places worldwide. Connect to the site for the full low-down.

Mega Grip   http://www.megagrip.co.uk
Dedicated to climbing and associated activities, including topographical information.

Mountain Guide   http://mtn-guide.com
Probably the most complete guide to summer mountain resorts in North America.

Rock & Ice
http://www.rockandice.com

A flashy and interesting magazine for rock climbers everywhere.

For the opposite of climbing, try Caves and Caving in the UK at http://www.sat.dundee.ac.uk/~arb/speleo.html. A totally comprehensive guide for anyone daft enough to want to climb down big holes in the ground.

Sobek Mountain Travel
http://www.mtsobek.com

Thirty years of mountain travel experience packed into an impressive site.

Cycling

Alaskan All Season Cycling
http://www.sketers.com/alaskabike.html

Winter mountain biking in Alaska sounds a bit extreme. But if you want somewhere a little different to pedal around, this website lights the way.

Back Road Travel in Sweden
http://members.aol.com/cfranzel/backroad.htm

A straightforward and basic website offering the chance to get off the beaten track by bicycle in Sweden.

Bicycle Beano Cycling Tours
http://www.kc3.co.uk/beano

On-road bicycle tours of Wales with the accent on relaxation and vegetarian food. Evocative pictures and full itinerary details.

Bicycle Tour Checklist
http://www-math.science.unitn.it/Bike/General/Packing_List.html

A straightforward list of things needed on a long-distance bicycle tour.

Bike Treks
http://www.angelfire.com/sk/biketreks

Pedal-powered safaris in the national parks and game reserves of Kenya.

Boomerang Bicycle Tours   http://www.ozemail.com.au/~ozbike

Tours, FAQs, links and news about Australian cycling all on a neat little website. Very quick to load and easy on the eye.

Club Toscana   http://www.clubtoscana.com

A range of cycling tours exclusively in Italy. An informative site offering the options of women only and family rides.

Country Lanes   http://dspace.dial.pipex.com/countrylanes

If the cycle tours of the UK are as well organised as the website then we reckon you'll be well pleased.

Cycle America   http://www.pedalthepeaks.com

Coast-to-coast, cross-state, cycle/camping combos and national park tours are all offered by this specialist company. The information is logically presented and quick to load.

OK, so it's a powered cycle, but you'll need one for the 'Trail of the Trolls'. Motorbiking in the mountain regions of Norway with Beach's Motorcycle Adventures – check it out at http://www.beachs-mca.com.

Country Spokes   http://users.ccnet.com/~cspokes

Gourmet cycling holidays in California, featuring good food, good company and, er, bicycles.

Freewheeling Adventures   http://www.freewheeling.ca

A Canadian company offering van-supported cycling tours of Atlantic Canada, Europe, Israel and Mexico. An exceptionally fast-loading site that most definitely isn't pedal powered.

Mountain Biking in the Himalayas   http://www.bluedome.co.uk/interest/mounbike/mbxhim.htm

Apparently a mountain biker's dream destination, and here's all you need to know about it.

One World Bicycle Expeditions   http://www.bikethailand.com

Explore the back roads and remote villages of Thailand by bike. Superb photography doesn't seem to slow down this otherwise very basic site.

Rough Tracks   http://www.rough-tracks.co.uk

If you prefer cycling off the beaten track rather than on the road then these mountain bike holiday specialists are the people for you.

Diving

Aquaholics   http://www.flash.net/~table

They admit that they are addicted to scuba diving and it shows in this excellent dive site.

Aquanaut   http://www.aquanaut.com

Another diver's delight, including looks at marine life, training and medical matters.

Aqua Trek   http://www.aquatrek.com

Diving holidays in Fiji for all levels of experience, from beginner to big headed.

Caribbean Dive Vacations   http://www.caradonna.com

The annoying animation aside, a good place to start if you fancy diving in the Caribbean.

Cayman Diving Lodge   http://www.divecdl.com

Oh, boy – one look at the beautiful photos on this website and you want to book up on the spot. The best diving in the Cayman Islands is 'our front yard', they proclaim.

The Bay Islands Beach Resort in Honduras welcomes disabled guests, with dive staff trained by the Handicapped Scuba Association. More information for able-bodied and disabled divers alike from http://www.bibr.com.

Crystal Divers   http://www.crystaldivers.com
Dive holidays in the waters around Fiji. A truly beautiful site that
really makes you want to go there.

Dive Guide International   http://www.diveguide.com
Click on the beach huts, get information on dive trips and diving
equipment.

Lyonesse Scuba Centre   http://www.lyonesse.co.uk
On Cornwall's Land's End peninsula, Lyonesse provides courses by
qualified trainers, wreck exploration and drift diving.

Regal Holidays   http://www.regal-diving.co.uk
If an underwater holiday sounds like fun then these diving
specialists can help. For total beginners and Jacques Cousteau-level
divers alike.

Fishing

Aurora Tours   http://www.ring.net/~aurora
Some broken English and pretty basic website design just adds
colour to this company offering fishing tours of Croatia.

Complete Fishing Tours   http://www.fishingtours.com.au
Complete, that is, if your world starts and ends at Australia. That
little nit-pick aside, the website offers lots of fishing tours for the
Aussie angler.

Fish Internet Australia   http://www.fishnet.com.au
Aussie carp safaris as well as a pro-angler guide, fish file and
picture gallery.

Fishing   http://www.pvisuals.
Online   com/fishing/online/main.html
Everything you need to plan a fishing vacation to Canada. Guides
to fly-fishing, resorts and species as well as links to all kinds of
online fishing resources.

Indian Ocean Angling   http://www.
Adventures   webpro.co.za/clients/flyfish
A very colourful and fishy guide to saltwater fly-fishing in Kenya,
Mozambique, the Seychelles and South Africa.

Point Loma   http://www.
Sportfishing   pointlomasportfishing.com
No-nonsense, very basic but rewarding website that provides the
low-down on deep-sea fishing trips in California and Baja Mexico.

Rod and Reel Adventures   http://www.rodreeladventures.com
Worldwide fishing and travel specialists with fourteen years in the
business.

Worldwide   http://www.
Fishing   worldwidefishing.com
A specialist online directory for all things fishy, including travel
information if you 'travel' into the onsite search engine.

Hiking

Adventure Line   http://www.chycor.co.uk/adventureline
Adventure walking holidays in Cornwall on the south coast of
England.

Adventure Trekking   http://www.
Worldwide   travelsource.com/trekking
Click on one of the link buttons to reveal details of various walking
holidays. A tad simplistic but it works.

American Long Distance   http://www.gorp.com/
Hikers Association   nonprof/aldhaw
News, trail reviews, tips and tricks – and even a long-distance
hiker's cookbook.

British Walking Tours   http://www.bctwalk.com
Scenic explorations on coastal and country footpaths around

the UK and, bizarrely for a company called British Coastal Trails, continental Europe.

Bushwalking in Australia   http://www.bushwalking.org.au
A haphazard site with some broken links, but the webmaster's passion shines through and there are gems here for the genuine bushwalking enthusiast.

European Walking Tours   http://www.gorp.com/ewt
Ideal if you love to go a wandering in Europe, specifically France, Italy and Switzerland.

Hiking Vacations http://www.teleport.com/~walking/trek.shtml
A selection of 'treks and tours' for the walking-holiday enthusiast including the rather risky sounding 'walking safari in Zimbabwe'

If you fancy walking across the UK you will need to know about these long-distance footpaths. The Long Distance Footpath Guide is at http://www.bluedome.co.uk/interest/trekking/treklong.htm..

Jack the Ripper Ghostwalk   http://www.rippingyarns.8m.com
The guides show you gruesome Victorian photos of the victims as they lead you around Jack the Ripper's London haunts. We are not at all surprised that they claim to be the only company to do this.

RailTrails   http://www.railtrails.org
A very different and appealing way to see the US, by walking a network of disused railway lines.

The Earth Is Yours   http://www.mcs.net/~teiywt
Walking tours mainly in the US and Mexico, but also Ireland and New Zealand. A good FAQ answers all your questions.

TrailPlace   http://www.trailplace.com
The art of 'thru-hiking' the Appalachian Trail. That's walking the complete 2,000 miles or so of it, in case you were wondering.

ScotWalk
http://www.scotwalk.co.uk

Learn something and keep fit at the same time. Hillwalking in the beautiful countryside of Scotland, with heritage talks.

Transcotland
http://www.transcotland.com

Self-guided walking tours in the Scottish Borders, Highlands and Islands. The company arranges the accommodation, baggage transfer and route mapping. You do the walking.

Naturism

Be warned that, by the very subject of this category, some of these sites may contain images of nudity.

A Bare Affair
http://www.bareaffair.com

A company that books discount holidays where the clothing is either optional or outlawed. Site navigation is simple but information is lacking in places.

Fantastic Voyages
http://www.fantasticvoyages.com/nudetours

A site that is very easy to navigate and which offers details of nudist and clothing-optional holidays at various resorts.

No Pockets Charters
http://www.nopockets.com

Cruising on some of the world's finest yachts in hot locations without clothes is No Pockets' speciality. Just take plenty of high-factor sunscreen.

Peng Travel
http://www.pengtravel.co.uk

Let it all hang out while you are away, literally, with a naturist holiday in Europe or the Americas.

The Naturist Society
http://www.naturist.com

All the best places to holiday in the nuddy. And the obligatory pictures of people shopping without any clothes on.

Through Our Eyes   http://www.cap-d-agde.com
The world capital of nudism, with 40,000 naturists and 3 miles of sandy beach to accommodate them.

Photography

Arizona Photo Excursions   http://www.photoexcursions.com
Architectural and landscape-oriented tours of Arizona under the watchful eye of tour guide and photographer Pam Singleton.

French Foto Tours   http://www.frenchfototours.com
Professional smudger-hosted photographic workshops in France, Greece, Italy and Mexico.

Shutter Chances   http://www.shutterchances.com.au
Explore the hidden treasures and colour of Africa, Australia, Japan and New Zealand.

Tanzania Photographic Safaris   http://www.africanphotos.com
African photo safaris operating out of a tented camp in the shade of a banyan tree on which Ernest Hemingway once carved his initials.

The PhotoTour   http://www.
Network   voyagers.com/voyagers/photwork.htm
Workshops ranging from nature photography tutorials to digital imaging. Uninspiring but functional.

Riding

Apache Stables   http://www.apachestables.com
Various riding jaunts around the Grand Canyon South Rim trail. If the photos on the website are anything to go by, you get a genuine cowboy to lead your group as well.

Discover Wales on   http://www.
Horseback   ponytrek.freeserve.co.uk
Horse riding or pony trekking – if you're hot to trot in Wales, these people can help.

Drumgooland House
http://www.travel-ireland.com/drumhrse

Horseback holidays in Ireland.

Equestrian Holidays in Ireland
http://www.ehi.ie

A country known for its horses, so where better to holiday on horseback?

Equestrian Safaris
http://www.sb.net/jan

Get past the annoying animated horses on the homepage and you soon discover a superb site detailing horse-riding holidays on the slopes of Mt Meru Volcano, Tanzania.

Equitrek
http://www.equitrek.com.au

Horse riding in an exotic location. Equitrek offers horsey holidays in the Australian outback for the true spirit of adventure.

Horses North
http://www.gorp.com/horsesnorth

Horse treks not found anywhere else on earth. A colourful site detailing horse treks around Iceland.

Mopani Park Bush Camp Kwekwe
http://wwwzimbabwe.net/.tourism/budget/Mopani/mopani_index.htm

Horse riding safaris in Zimbabwe. Including short rides, one-day safaris and overnight stays. The river rides, which let you swim with the horses, sound truly inspiring.

Ohe'o Stables
http://www.maui.net/~ray

Horse riding in Hawaii, the Haleakala National Park to be precise. Offering ocean and spectacular waterfall views.

The Spirit of Exmoor
http://www.homestead.com/spirtofexmoor/main.html

Riding holidays for grown ups, covering the moors, woodland and rivers of Exmoor, North Devon.

Safaris

Ad-Ventura Safaris
http://www.safhire.co.za

Do-it-yourself safaris in South Africa. They hire the all-terrain vehicles and point you in the right direction; you drive the thing and try not to be eaten by lions.

Africa Safari
http://www.tanzania-web.com/worldarc

Tailor-made African safaris are this firm's speciality, along with taking photographs of lions and elephants.

Africa Safari Specialists
http://www.safaris.com

Safari means 'journey' in Swahili – a fact gleaned from this website, which is also a good place to start a journey deep into the African bush.

Australian Natural History Safaris
http://www.anhs.com.au

Tropical rain forest tours in small groups, for a truly personal touch.

Bearman
http://www.gomontana.com/bearman

Let the Bearman be your guide to watching grizzly and black bears in Yellowstone Park. Also details of the wild wolves of Yellowstone, but without a Wolfman to help you – for which we should be grateful.

Bush Homes of East Africa
http://www.bushhomes.com

An unusual custom safari specialist that offers the chance to stay in private homes as well as ranches and lodges throughout Kenya and Tanzania.

Churchill Nature Tours
http://www.churchillnaturetours.com/polarbear.html

Specially organised tours to see the polar bears of Canada's accessible Arctic coast. A basic but efficient website tells you all you need to know.

EcoAfrica
http://www.ecoafrica.com

Tailor-made nature-friendly safaris to South Africa.

Rare Earth Explorations   http://www.gorp.com/rareearth
A very easy-to-explore website that provides details of varied eco-friendly and nature-oriented safaris in Africa and India. We liked the sound of the gorilla trekking in Kenya.

Serengeti Balloon Safaris   http://www.balloonsafaris.com
Tanzanian sky safaris in a balloon capable of holding 28 passengers.

SWA Safaris   http://www.iwwn.com.na/swasaf
Privately organised safari tours through Namibia to Victoria Falls.

Wildscapes Safaris   http://www.ozemail.com.au/~wildscap
Various Australian outback adventures are on offer here, including 'platypus research in the tropics' and 'the rainforest at night'.

Sailing

Aladdin Cruises   http://wwmarine.com/aladdin
The luxury-class, fully-crewed way to sail. Hey, why do it yourself if you can afford a crew – right?

BahamasVacation   http://www.bahamavacation.com
Charter a captained sailboat and stay in a rented cottage in the Bahamas. Nice site, lovely idea.

Blue Water Charters   http://www.
Tall Ship Adventures   tallshipadventures.com
A maritime feel to the design of this site, detailing holidays on board the tall ship Sir Francis Drake. A nice feature is a very slick slide-show tour of the ship itself.

Caribbean Yacht Vacations   http://www.whidbey.com/cyv
Bareboat or crewed sailing yachts in the Caribbean.

Sailing Holidays   http://www.
in Tonga   magna.com.au/~hideaway/tbu_sail.html
Charter a boat, crewed or otherwise, in Tonga.

SaltySeas   http://www.saltyseas.com

This site started life as a personal account of sailing charters in Greece, but has expanded considerably to include worldwide sailing guides, travelogues, website links and a bookshop.

World Wide Sail   http://www.duhe.com

Wait for the Java-powered map to load (sigh) and then choose your ideal destination for a sailing holiday. But don't bother with South America – at the time of writing, they haven't got anything there.

Whale Watching

Alaska Whale Watching   http://www.1alaskafishing.com

As well as sports fishing, this charter company also offers a whale-watching tour in the icy waters of Alaska.

Captain John   http://www.
Boats   whalewatchingplymouth.com

Departing from Plymouth, Massachusetts for the famous whales of Cape Cod. Presumably cod watching isn't a big hit with thrill-seeking tourists.

Hervey Bay Whale   http://www.
Watching   peg.apc.org/~frasertravel/whale.htm

All your options for humpback holidays in this Australian location that has been christened the 'whale watching capital of the world'.

Lunenburg Whale   http://www.
Watching Tours   outdoorns.com/whalewatching

Fin, pilot, minke and humpbacks – up close and natural in Nova Scotia.

Seasmoke Whale Watching   http://www.seaorca.com

Sailing tours of the Johnstone Strait in British Columbia, the place to see the orcas or killer whale.

Winter Sports

1Ski   http://www.1ski.com
Probably the biggest skiing and snowboarding travel and holiday service on the web. Resort guides, snow reports and more.

Altours   http://www.altours.co.uk
Another skiing specialist that will help you get piste in France, Italy and the USA.

Board the World   http://www.boardtheworld.com
A global travel guide for people who like to slide downhill on one big ski thing.

Frontier Ski   http://www.frontier-ski.co.uk
A British company offering ski holidays in Alaska and Canada.

Rocky Mountain   http://www.
Adventures   rockymountain.co.uk
Snowboarding holidays in the Rocky Mountains, where else with a website name like this? Click on the slipping snowy bloke for the info.

Skiers Travel Bureau   http://skiers-travel.co.uk
An excellent site, with comprehensive information on skiing and snowboarding holidays and the latest resort deals on the first page.

Snow Safaris   http://www.snowsafari.co.za
Serious ski trips for serious skiers. Unusual locations like the former USSR, and unusual adventure tours including heli-skiing trips.

Ten Rules For   http://www.
Skiing Beginners   virgin.net/travel/features/arc_682.htm
The essential list to save broken bones and broken relationships on the piste. Above all, remember: 'Don't buy a one-piece ski suit you might never use again'.

rec.climbing
uk.rec.climbing
Barefaced cheek.

rec.scuba
uk.rec.scuba
Diving discussions.

alt.fishing
rec.outdoors.fishing
uk.rec.fishing.coarse
uk.rec.fishing.game
uk.rec.fishing.sea
Fishy business.

uk.rec.cycling
On your bike.

rec.skiing
rec.skiing.snowboard
Slidin' thru snow.

uk.rec.birdwatching
Tweet tweet.

uk.rec.sailing
We are sailing, we are sailing...

alt.rec.hiking
uk.rec.walking
Blisters R Us.

6//GETTING THERE, STAYING THERE

Making your own travel arrangements has many advantages. Instead of being locked into a package tour schedule or a travel agent's itinerary, you can choose exactly where you will stay, how long for and how you will get there – and change your plans halfway through if you feel like it. But many people have been put off the do-it-yourself route by the sheer time and effort needed to hunt down the right hotel, the best deal for your choice of transport, a decent hire car and all the rest.

The Internet has changed all that, by plugging the consumer into the same travel booking database as the travel agents. There are two big international reservation systems, called WorldSpan and SABRE. Whenever you use an online flight booking service, your query will be referred to these systems.

Scheduled airlines allocate seat prices on a complex basis. As a rule of thumb, the seats that get sold first get sold cheaper than those nearer departure. If you can't book far in advance, then use the reservation database systems from the flight booking websites to compare prices from both airlines and specialist 'late availability' services.

When you arrive you'll need somewhere to stay – and again, the net doesn't let you down. Every conceivable type of lodging is available online, from five star hotels to treetop lodgings in the canopy of the Amazon rainforest. What's more, in most cases you can take advantage of discounted rates and online booking as well.

The travel agents aren't throwing in the towel yet, though. In fact they are well represented in cyberspace, from the well-known high-street names that have a shop window on the web to specialist services that don't trade terrestrially. The best of these are the all-in-one sites, where you can research your destination, compare flights and accommodation and book the lot via your PC. Because there's no retail space to rent, these are cheaper to run than any terrestrial shop – and the savings are passed on to the consumer.

//ADDRESS BOOK

Starting Points

A2B Travel   http://www.a2btravel.com
One of the biggest online agencies in the UK. A2B is a slick and quick gateway to holidays, flights and hotel rooms.

Accommodation Search Engine   http://asa.net
A search engine dedicated to finding any kind of accommodation, in any destination you care to mention. Around 40,000 establishments are listed, so you stand a pretty good chance of finding a match.

Airlines of the Web   http://flyaow.com
This site links to just about every airline with an online presence. If you need to find a specific airline in a rush then this is the right place to start.

Expedia   http://www.expedia.com
This fast, efficient and cheap service is the perfect example of the new breed of travel agency. Flight reservations, hotel room booking, car rentals and more – all from one central site.

Travelocity   http://www.travelocity.co.uk
Uses the SABRE travel agents' booking system and offers similar services to Expedia, but is slower to load and less intuitive to use.

//GETTING THERE

Online Travel Agents

American Express Travel   http://travel.americanexpress.com
That'll do nicely. Holidays, flights and hotels – and you don't need to be an AMEX cardholder to use it.

ATM Travel   http://www.atmtravel.co.uk
Late offers and Las Vegas specials from a simple UK travel site.

Bargain Holidays   http://www.bargainholidays.com
Colourful and feature-packed site that loads quickly and certainly comes up with the goods – lots of cheap holidays.

BucketShop   http://www.bucketshop.com
Part of the Association of Special Fares Agents, but we still prefer the term 'bucket shop'. Discounted airfare companies from around the planet.

Budget Travel   http://www.budgettravel.com
For the terminally stingy. Save money before you go on holiday and when you get there.

Can Be Done Travel   http://www.canbedone.co.uk
A travel operator specialising in holidays and tours for people with disabilities. No online booking yet, but invaluable advice and ideas.

Club 18-30   http://www.club18-30.co.uk
Sun, sand, sex and booze-filled holidays for young adults. The website's pretty lively too.

Destination Group   http://www.destination-group.com
Self-drive motor homes, cruises, rail tickets and flights – in fact, most types of travel to far-flung destinations.

Discount Holidays & Flights   http://www.dhf.co.uk
Booking with 500 airlines and assorted holiday deals. All from an easy-to-use and enjoyable site, with competitions and editorial.

Disney World Planner   http://disney.go.com
Use the interactive trip wizard to create a personal holiday plan
that you can then book online. As long as it's to Walt Disney World,
Disneyland or Disneyland Paris, that is.

Holiday Deals   http://www.holidaydeals.co.uk
From the Co-op, more holidays at the cheap end of the market.

Instant Holidays   http://www.instant-holidays.com
A clever 'holiday search' database that will scan 70,000 offers from
leading tour operators to match your request.

Internet Holidays   http://www.holiday.co.uk
A simple site with a search facility to find the right bargain break.
Shame they have to telephone you to confirm booking
arrangements, though.

Find out the speed, altitude, estimated time of arrival and even type of
aircraft for any flight number at Flight Tracker (http://www.thetrip.com/
usertools/flighttracking).

Internet Travel Auctions   http://www.holidayauctions.net
Now here's something different. Bid for holidays in a wide range of
categories including golf breaks, ski trips and cruises.

Just Lanzarote   http://www.justlanzarote.demon.co.uk
Holidays to Fuerteventura as well as Lanzarote, but then that
would probably have been too long to fit in the browser address
window.

Silk Steps   http://www.silk-steps.co.uk
A company specialising in tailor-made tours of the Far East and the
Horn of Africa. Not cheap, but not your run-of-the-mill package
holiday either.

Teletext Holidays   http://www.teletext.co.uk/holidays
Bizarrely, you can indeed use Teletext on the web to book your
bargain break.

Thomas Cook Online   http://www.thomascook.co.uk
Well-known high-street travel agent sells insurance, holidays, late availability bargains and timeshares. They stop short of accepting online orders, preferring to complete your booking on the phone.

Travel Select   http://www.travelselect.co.uk
Dead simple to use front end backed up by an impressive range of features. Just click the tab that intrigues you. Choose from flights, car hire, Eurostar, hotels, exchange rates and a holiday planner.

TravelWeb   http://www.travelweb.com
Dedicated to hotel and flight reservations, with the fastest hotel search in the business.

U Can Travel   http://www.netos.com/uct
A site specifically designed for the student traveller. Which means cheap holidays to interesting places, with some work thrown in to help cover the cost.

Flights

Aer Lingus   http://www.aerlingus.ie
Ireland's national airline in all its green glory. Schedules and reservations plus special offers and travel insurance facilities.

Aeroflot   http://www.aeroflot.co.uk
Superbly swish site for the Russian international airline. Home country information on offer as well as plane tickets.

Air Canada   http://www.aircanada.ca
News, schedules, fares – plus reservations and tickets using a 'cyber ticket office', which works well, despite the tedious name.

Air France   http://www.airfrance.co.uk
Trip-planning and flight-status facilities but no online booking unfortunately. Watch out for buttons that change language of their own accord.

British Airways   http://www.british-airways.com
Schedules, airport information and online booking, plus city guides
and in-flight movie details on a very-well-executed website.

British Midland   http://www.britishmidland.co.uk
A nice-looking site with booking via the CyberSeat system.

Cathay Pacific   http://www.cathaypacific-air.com
Schedules, seating plans, destination tours and online booking.
Plus a holiday planning service and special Internet deals.

Continental Airlines   http://www.continental.com
A very slick site with good search facilities. Corporate and travel
information, special deals and holiday flights, online reservations
and a flight status indicator.

Delta Air Lines   http://www.delta-air.com
Straightforward searching and an interactive assistant to help out if
you run into trouble.

Easyjet   http://www.easyjet.com
A low-cost airline but a highly workable website. No fuss here:
straight into the business of finding flights and booking tickets – all
in double quick time.

A British Airways trainer who advises air crew on safety matters
shares her insider knowledge on the In-flight Safety Page at
http://www.plsys.co.uk/~anna/inflight.htm. It's well worth a read.

Finnair   http://www.finnair.co.uk
Far more information on all aspects of the company than you need
to know. Flights to Finland are in there somewhere too.

Go   http://www.go-fly.com
British Airways no-frills airline has a suitably no-frills website. All
the information you could require, and an online booking
department too.

Iceland Air   http://www.icelandair.co.uk
A small country, a small airline, but a big website – with a gazetteer of information about Iceland and online booking.

KLM   http://www.klm.com
A comprehensive site with online reservation facilities. Not all double Dutch once you select your home country from the drop-down list on the main page.

Need some reassurance that the skies we fly in are a safe place to be? Nowhere better to get it than from the Civil Aviation Authority website at http://www.caa.co.uk.

Lufthansa   http://www.lufthansa.com
A nice clean site with timetables and bookings. Added extras here include a news ticker and an archive photo gallery of the fleet past and present.

Ryan Air   http://www.ryanair.com
Ireland's second largest airline brings low-cost fares to a wider audience.

Singapore Air   http://www.singaporeair.com
Schedules and route maps, plus guides to local sites in Singapore. Online booking involves (seamlessly) connecting to a separate website.

TWA   http://www.twa.com
Trans World Airlines offer special 'dot.com.deals' when you book your flights direct from this flashy but slow website.

United Airlines   http://www.ual.com
Extremely comprehensive site from one of the world's biggest airlines. Right down to seat maps of the aircraft and locations of laptop PC power points.

Virgin Atlantic   http://www.fly.virgin.com

A very snazzy, well very red actually, website – and excellent online booking and information resources.

Flight Finders and Ticket Bookers

Air Tickets Direct   http://www.airtickets.co.uk

Another value-added site offering more than just cheap tickets. Extras here include info on airport parking, hotels and travel insurance.

Deckchair.com   http://www.deckchair.com

There's nothing scruffy about Bob Geldof's down-and-dirty, no-frills flight booking service.

Epicurious All-in-One   http://www.travel.epicurious.com/travel

Follow the links to sign up here for email notification of discount deals from eight airlines. All from the same page for the truly lazy online bargain hunter.

Farebase   http://www.farebase.net

Scheduled, charter and last-minute flights from the company that also supplies airfare data to the UK travel industry.

What do people really think about the airlines they've used? Find out at the Gomez Travel Scorecard (http://www.scorecard.com/Travel).

Flight Bids   http://www.flightbids.co.uk

Here's an unusual one. Submit the price you want to pay for your flight and an agent will get back to you if the price is OK with them. Silly offers won't get you anywhere, but pitch it about right and you could be lucky.

Flightbookers   http://www.flightbookers.co.uk

They claim an amazing 1.2 million discounted airfares. The site itself is rather too fussy and crowded, but we can forgive them that, especially at those prices.

The Air Transport Users Council (http://www.auc.org.uk) is an excellent friend if you need to know what to do if your luggage gets lost or a flight is cancelled.

Lastminute.Com   http://www.lastminute.com
As the name suggests, this is for booking those last-minute flights and holidays. Good bargains abound, but shop around the web as the prices are not always the cheapest.

Student Flights   http://www.studentflights.co.uk
Student and youth discount fares on most scheduled airlines. Not the most intuitive of site designs and the lack of online booking is disappointing.

The Airline Network   http://www.airnet.co.uk
An independent travel company providing discounted fares from 100 scheduled airlines, with a fast search facility and straightforward online booking.

International Airports

Australia

Brisbane International Airport   http://www.bne.com.au
The website is divided into corporate, travel and shopping sections, which helps you get to the right information quickly.

Sydney Airport   http://www.acay.com.au/~willt/yssy
A thoughtful signpost on the front door lets enthusiasts and visitors take separate routes into the site. The A-Z terminal guide, following the visitor's route, is an essential printout for any Sydney-bound traveller.

Belgium

Brussels Airport http://www.brusselsairport.be

A well-thought-out website that includes nice touches such as information on peak days, airport statistics and an online telephone directory.

Canada

Montreal Airports http://www.admtl.com/index-e.html

Dorval and Mirabel get a straightforward information makeover here. Once past the impressive home page things get a little more basic, but nonetheless useful.

Vancouver International Airport http://www.yvr.ca

'Feature packed' doesn't do it justice. There's even a section on airport art and another just for cruise ship passengers arriving at the airport.

France

Paris Airports http://www.paris-airports.com

Roissy, Charles de Gaulle and Orly get equally comprehensive coverage on this slick site. Access, car parking, bars, shops and hotels are all here, along with the timetables of course.

Denmark

Copenhagen Airport http://www.cph.dk

The entry page fools you into thinking there isn't much on offer here, but click on a link such as 'general information' and you soon discover that the depth of information is actually astounding.

Germany

Frankfurt http://www.frankfurt-airport.de

Another very-well-designed site that is as easy on the eye as it is easy to navigate. Special needs information and an interactive travel planner are nice touches.

Stuttgart   **http://www.stuttgart-airport.de**

Departure and arrival boards as you see them in the airport plus big, well-marked buttons for navigation make this website particularly easy to use.

Greece

Athens International   **http://www.**
Airport   **athensairport-2001.gr**

Take either the flashy 'flash enhanced' multimedia option or the speedier straightforward route. The information about this new airport, opening in March 2001, is top-notch either way.

Hong Kong

Hong Kong International Airport   **http://www.hkairport.com**

Slick, sleek and speedy. If only all airport sites were as well thought out and implemented as this. The maps and guides are particularly impressive.

Ireland

Dublin   **http://www.dublinairport.com**

Real-time flight information and detailed airport maps mark Dublin airports website out as a good 'un.

Israel

Ben Gurion Airport   **http://www.ben-gurion-airport.com**

Arrivals, departures and timetables are to be expected. Parking, pre-flight service, restaurant and shopping information are all nice bonuses. Make sure you click the US flag first, though, to get the English language version.

Italy

Milan **http://www.airwise.**
Malpensa **com/airports/europe/MXP**
Transportation, car rental, accommodation and history seem to get as much coverage as the terminals and flight info. But it's all very consumer friendly and well written.

Netherlands

Amsterdam Schiphol **http://www.schiphol.nl**
A feature-packed site that includes a 3D tour, traffic information, weather reports and a chat room in addition to the usual airport information staples.

Rotterdam **http://www.rotterdam-airport.nl**
Click on the English flag first, and then enjoy this very quick and highly interactive airport guide.

New Zealand

Auckland International **http://www.auckland-**
Airport **airport.co.nz**
A no-nonsense website that balances consumer and corporate information. Airport maps and terminal guides are much appreciated.

Norway

Oslo **http://www.osl.no**
Follow the 'English' route for a fairly basic, and Java-dependent, guide to the airport and its facilities.

Portugal

Macau International **http://www.**
Airport **macau-airport.gov.mo**
Flights, tourist information, airport guides and weather forecasts are the order of the day for this easy-access site.

South Africa

Johannesburg   **http://www.**
International Airport   **airports.co.za/acsa/jia**

Maps, weather reports, parking arrangements and a lecture on security feature alongside the terminal and flight information.

South Korea

Kimpo International   **http://www.kimpo-**
Airport   **airport.co.kr/ENG**

An extremely fast-loading site, thanks to its basic design and lack of overbearing graphics. There is no lacking in depth of customer service information, though.

Switzerland

Geneva International Airport   **http://www.gva.ch**

Ignore the cheesy 'airport of summits' pun on the entry page and you have a slick menu-driven website that delivers the informational goods with style.

Zurich   **http://www.zurich-airport.com**

All the information you could possibly require can be found on this graphics-heavy, but still swift, site.

Thailand

Bangkok International   **http://www.**
Airport   **airportthai.or.th/html/bkk.html**

Slick design and no-nonsense content, once you get past the self-congratulatory front door that is. All you need to know if you are planning to fly into Bangkok.

British Airports Authority   http://www.baa.co.uk
The company that operates all three of London's airports and many
others, including Edinburgh, Glasgow and Southampton.

Belfast International Airport   http://www.bial.co.uk
Featuring an in-depth but boring section on cargo facts and
figures.

Birmingham International Airport   http://www.bhx.co.uk
It doesn't hurt to check out the airport facilities before you get
there. Details of taxis, disability facilities, baggage trolleys and the
shops, amongst others, here.

If you need to get somewhere inland in a hurry then it's hard to think of
a quicker travel option than a helicopter. So why not hire your very own
chopper? No online booking but plenty of information to get you
started. See Helicopter Hire at http://www.users.globalnet.co.uk/~helico.

Leeds Bradford International Airport   http://www.lbia.co.uk
A very comprehensive site covering all aspects of the airport, from
parking the car to catching the flight.

London City Airport   http://www.londoncityairport.com
The airport may be small but the website is big on facts and
features. Schedules, transportation and facilities including online
flight booking.

Luton Airport   http://www.london-luton.co.uk
A very slick site, with all the usual info.

Manchester Airport   http://www.manairport.co.uk
Apparently Manchester is the 'gateway to the UK'. That wild claim
aside, the rest of the site is useful for anyone using this
busy airport.

USA

Dallas Fort Worth http://www.dfwairport.com

Almost too much information to take in easily but, the crowded design apart, you can't fault this comprehensive guide for the Dallas flyer.

Denver International Airport http://flydenver.com

Four entry points provide quick access to information on the weather, car parking, airport guides and flights.

Honolulu International Airport http://kumu.icsd. hawaii.gov/dot/hono.htm

Plenty of information, but all on one very long page makes it slow to load and difficult to navigate.

Miami International http://www.miami-airport.com

Attention to detail in terminal maps and passenger information is only matched by a sense of fun. Enter 'Wally Wing's Playground' to see what we mean!

JFK http://www.jfkiat.com

A disappointing website for such a famous and busy New York airport. The information available is let down by the poor presentation and lack of any real interactivity.

LaGuardia http://www.panynj.gov/laguardiaairport

A smaller NY airport, but a much better website. Excellent maps and guides plus links to other online resources for New York and New Jersey.

Seattle-Tacoma http://www.portseattle.org/seatac

Good use of Java in providing a fully interactive airport map, and plenty of good old-fashioned text covering all aspects of the airport for the non-Java equipped online traveller.

RAIL TRAVEL

British Railways

Central Trains http://www.centraltrains.co.uk
Interactive train maps, a user's guide to tickets, and a message that clean trains are a priority. Timetables, yes – online ticketing, no.

First Great Western http://www.great-western-trains.co.uk
A cool site with whooshing train animation and some fancy menus, backed up with solid information but no online ticketing.

Flying Scotsman http://www.flyingscotsman.com
One of the world's most famous steam trains is now operating again. Booking information can be found at this official site, which is under new ownership.

Great Eastern Railways http://www.ger.co.uk
A website in two flavours. Simple for speed, and enhanced for showing off. We preferred the speedy route to fares and timetables.

GNER http://www.gner.co.uk
An excellent 'how's my train running?' feature updates you on all departures and arrivals from any given station.

Midland Mainline http://mml.rail.co.uk
Real-time train information, timetables and station guides, but no online booking here.

Northern Ireland Railways http://www.nirailways.co.uk
A network map and some corporate information. Otherwise a disappointing effort that even asks you to phone for timetable information, so don't even think about online ticket purchase.

RailInfo http://www.railinfo.freeserve.co.uk/railtravel
A useful guide to using the railways of Britain, with almost enough detail to satisfy a dedicated trainspotter.

Railtrack Timetables http://www.railtrack.co.uk
Faster than phoning and quicker than queuing. What's more, the timetable information here tends to be accurate as well.

ScotRail http://www.scotrail.co.uk
Both West and North Highland lines plus Caledonian sleepers are covered here by ScotRail. Timetabling, but no online ticketing.

Thames Trains http://www.thamestrains.co.uk
A straightforward site with information on disabled facilities, taking cycles on trains and penalty fares. Plus the usual timetabling stuff.

Trainline http://www.thetrainline.com
Now this makes sense. One site from which you can get times, book tickets and reserve seats for any train operator in the UK.

Virgin Trains http://virgintrains.co.uk
Train times, fares and features – and an Internet ticketing service offering exclusive discounts for some online bookings.

International Railways

Amtrak Unlimited http://www.amtrak-trains.com
All you need to know about this legendary American rail company, with excellent links to route, fare and online reservation resources.

Australia's Great Train Journeys http://www.gsr.com.au
Timetables and fares, destinations and trains, and online booking forms for most Oz rail operators.

Belgian Railways http://www.b-rail.be
A fully loaded site covering international and domestic train travel including details of Eurostar, TGV and Thalys services.

Canadian Pacific Railway http://www.cpr.ca
CPR has taken the portal approach to the website, and so it's easy

to find just about anything you need to know about the company and its services.

Deutsche Bahn http://www.deutschebahn.de/home_e
A comprehensive and informative site, but finding the English language content is very hit and miss.

Euro Railways http://www.eurorailways.com
Good umbrella site for rail travel in Europe, with everything from high speed TGVs to the leisurely romance of the Orient Express. This is the place to find out about multi-country rail passes.

European National Railways and http://mercurio.iet.
Timetables unipi.it/misc
Timetables and associated railway company information for all the major services around Europe.

Eurotunnel http://www.eurotunnel.com
Operator of the channel tunnel offers a pleasant site that provides all the passenger information you'll need, plus online booking and freight details.

Grand Canyon Railway http://www.thetrain.com
A historic train ride to, and through, the Grand Canyon. Get the timetable and fare information here and take the virtual tour while you are at it.

Indian Railways http://www.trainweb.com/indiarail
An unofficial but absolutely essential guide to getting around on Indian railways. Timetables and maps are well presented and easy to find.

Indian Railways http://www.indianrailway.com
The official site is much slicker, but slow to load. A tourist info section and detailed timetables make it worth the wait, though.

Inland Railway Line
http://www.inlandsbanan.se/england.html

The website of the Trans-Siberian Railway of Sweden, which runs through 1,100 km of wilderness. No online booking, but plenty to make you wish there was.

InterRail
http://interrailer.net/english

How to travel throughout Europe for a month on a single railway ticket. For young people only.

Japan Train Travel
http://www.sfjnto.org

Superbly comprehensive, with links to the 'bullet train' timetables, airport shuttle services, national railway networks and details of fares and passes.

Kowloon-Canton Railway Corporation
http://www.kcrc.com

Not the quickest site we have visited, but it is in English and it is full of useful travel information.

New Zealand by Rail
http://byrail.wellington.net.nz

A simple, unofficial, guide to travelling across New Zealand by train. Good links and an attention to detail throughout.

Rail Connection
http://www.railconnection.com

A superb site featuring an interactive ticket collector who can help you to find the right rail pass at the best price for train travel across Europe.

RENFE, Spain
http://www.renfe.es/ingles

Timetables, fares and route information for the Spanish AVE, Grandes Lineas, Regionales and Cercanias train services.

SMRT, Singapore
http://www.smrt.com.sg

Travel and ticket information at the click of a mouse. Select a departure station and a destination and your fare is displayed along with the time it takes to travel.

SNCF, France http://www.sncf.fr/indexe.htm
An interactive journey planner includes timetable and fare information plus a comprehensive and essential passenger's guide.

TGV http://mercurio.iet.unipi.it/tgv/tgvindex.html
An unofficial but incredibly comprehensive and enthusiastic guide to the famous high-speed train and its routes.

Trans-Siberian http://www.trans-
Express siberian.co.uk/transsib.html
Experience Russia by train – all the staff of this travel specialist have done so. Click on an interactive ticket and get maps, routes, fares and timetables.

VIA Rail Canada http://www.viarail.ca
Railroad maps and schedules nestle alongside online ticketing services. A highly useful site for both tourist and business travellers to Canada.

Voyages Jules Verne http://www.vjv.co.uk
Among other things, these guys like to resurrect classic train journeys, like the London to Hong Kong overland route and the inaugural journey of the Orient Express.

World Subway http://metro.ratp.fr:10001/
Navigator bin/cities/english
This is a gem, with details of every underground railway system in the world. Enter the station you're leaving from and your destination station. It'll calculate your route, and tell you how long it'll take.

ON THE ROAD

Car Hire

Avis Online http://www.avis.co.uk
Nice site design with search and reservation facilities right on the

first page. Dig deeper for fleet details, rental locations and extras like maps and directions.

Budget Rent-A-Car http://www.drivebudget.com
Vehicle details change according to the country you select, which is nice – but only US residents can make online reservations.

Hertz http://www.hertz.co.uk
Everything you need to hire and book a car is here, but the confusing mix-and-match interface on the home page makes finding it a task rather than a pleasure.

Rentadeal.Com http://www.rentadeal.com
Tell them where you're going and what you want, and Rentadeal will provide details from a selection of car rental firms. Choose the one that suits and book online. Lots in the US, and coverage of major international cities too.

Street Eagle Motorcycle Rentals http://www.streeteagle.com
When in Florida, rent a Harley online and take the state by storm.

Route Planning

AA http://www.
Roadwatch theaa.co.uk/motoringandtravel/traffic
The AA's weekly list of roadworks to watch out for across the UK.

Roadwatch http://rwa.
America Direct metronetworks.com/rwadirect.html
It takes a while to get to this information: click on the map, then drill down to the state and eventually link to the right highway commission and construction sites. But it's worth it.

RAC Routeplanner http://www.rac.co.uk/html/services
No need to purchase expensive route planning software when the RAC will do it for free from the website. A bonus is the live traffic news provided here.

USA Driving Directions http://maps.americanexpress.com/travel_pers/mqtripplus

Enter a start and finish point anywhere in North America and this service will map out the route.

Bus and Coach Travel – UK

Busweb http://www.busweb.co.uk

Links to bus company sites around the world from this public-transport-obsessed website.

London Transport http://www.londontransport.co.uk

All you need to know about London buses (except why they always turn up in bunches) and tubes. A useful interactive journey planner is also provided.

National Express http://www.nationalexpress.co.uk

Timetables, online ticketing, reservations and plenty of suggestions for places to go by coach.

International Bus and Coach Travel

Arrow Line http://www.arrowline.com

Chartered and scheduled coach transport in North America: all the details are on this easy to access site.

Baz Bus http://www.icon.co.za/~bazbus

A bus that lets you hop on and hop off just about all of South Africa. Aimed at the backpacker, but of use to any adventurous tourist.

Buslines Australia http://www.buslines.com.au

A one-stop shop for Australian bus information. The website covers scheduled, charter and tours, as long as a bus is involved.

China Motor Bus Company http://www.great-china.net/cmb

Operating since 1933, the China Bus Company has routes between mainland China and Hong Kong.

Costa Rican Buses   http://www.magic-bus.com/crbus.htm

A descriptive guide to bus travel in Costa Rica, with links to timetables.

Greyhound   http://www.greyhound.com

Probably the best-known bus service in the world. Greyhound buses cover the length and breath of the USA and all the fares and schedules are here.

Leipzig Bus Timetables   http://www.l.sda.de

Hit the 'welcome' link and the website changes to English. All the bus stuff can be found in the traffic section.

National Bus Company of Ireland   http://www.buseireann.ie

Routes, timetables, customer service and a friendly Irish welcome await visitors here.

Singapore Shuttle Bus   http://www.tibs.com.sg/ssb

Think of it as a park and ride scheme for Singapore and you'll have the shuttle bus sussed.

Sydney Buses   http://www.sydneybuses.nsw.gov.au

Routes, timetables and tickets available here, along with lost property information in the best bus company tradition.

Tica Bus   http://www.ticabus.com/Eindex.htm

A route guide and timetables for this bus company providing daily rides in Central American countries.

ON THE WATER

Luxury Cruises

Cunard Line   http://www.cunardline.com

The company that runs the celebrated QE2. The site features a 'cruise consultant' – actually a search engine in disguise, but it still helps you find the right cruise and the right time.

Cruise.Com http://www.cruise.com
The Internet's largest discount cruise seller, or so we're told. A useful source of information on cruise essentials like dinner menus and tipping as well.

Cruise Opinion http://www.cruiseopinion.com
A database of 3,000 cruise reviews from the people who know best – people who've been.

Cruise Pages http://www.travelpage.com/cruise
The low-down on high-class cruising. Hundreds of reviews of cruises, cruise ships and cruise lines.

Cruise Ship Center http://www.cruise2.com
Everything for the seafaring holidaymaker, right down to assorted cruise line cabin plans and dinner menus.

For a different view of the ocean wave, try travelling on a freighter or a scientific expedition ship. Try the Cruise and Freighter Travel Association (http://www.travltips.com) and the Internet Guide to Freighter Travel (http://people.we.mediaone.net/freighterman) for all the information you need.

P&O Cruise http://www.pocruises.com
Tour the fleet, taste life on board and explore the destinations covered. A simple and efficient website, but no real-time online booking. You can email reservations, which is a start.

Princess Cruises http://www.princess.com
A very blue website that does all it can to conjure up that floating feeling. Good itinerary and vessel information but lacking in booking facilities and, more worryingly, pricing details.

Windstar Cruise http://www.windstarcruises.com
A change from the ordinary cruise lines. Windstar have a 617-foot sail-powered cruiser that looks as impressive as she sounds.

Ferries

Brittany Ferries   http://www.brittany-ferries.com

Direct sailings from the UK to France and Spain. Plenty of special offers and fleet information but, like many ferry companies, no online booking yet.

EuroDrive   http://www.eurodrive.co.uk

Cheap fares across the channel by Eurostar, cross-channel ferry or Le Shuttle. Absolutely no frills at this site, just cheap prices.

Ferry Companies of the Web   http://www.ferrytravel.de

The title explains all – a guide to all the ferry operators with an online presence.

Greek Ferries   http://www.greekferries.gr

International ferries to and from Greece, plus domestic ferries between the Greek islands. A massive site that's packed with information. Good search facilities and online ticket purchase are a bonus.

Hoverspeed   http://www.hoverspeed.co.uk

Thirty-four daily departures from the UK to mainland Europe by hovercraft or catamaran.

Irish Ferries   http://www.irishferries.ie

Whether it's Ireland to Britain or vice-versa this well-indexed website has all the fares and timetables you need.

Stena Line   http://www.stenaline.co.uk

Vessels, ports, prices and timetables for ferry travel between UK, Irish and Dutch routes. And one of the few companies that let you book online.

Barges and Boats in the UK

British Waterways   http://www.british-waterways.org

The leisurely pace of life on a canal boat. Interactive canal and river maps and a search facility.

Canal Junction   http://www.canaljunction.com
A leisure directory and guide to the British canal network. Hire firms, 'hotel boats' and special offers on late availability holiday deals.

International Waterways

Amsterdam Canals   http://www.nbt.nl/NBT-amst-canals.html
A Java-heavy guide to the canals of Amsterdam. Options to explore them by cruise or 'water bike' available here.

Canal Society of Indiana   http://www.indcanal.org
Dedicated to preserving the Wabash & Erie, Central, Cross Cut and Whitewater canals of Indiana.

Canal Society of New Jersey   http://www.waterloovillage.
New Jersey   org/canal.asp
The history of the Morris canal that runs the route of Interstate 80, or used to at least.

Christianshavn's Canal   http://www.ravelinen.dk/his-6uk.htm
Better known as the Copenhagen-Amsterdam canal, Christianshavn is one of the three remaining central-Copenhagen canals.

Friends of the Delaware Canal   http://www.fodc.org
A real enthusiast's site, delivering an astonishing insight into the life and workings of this canal.

French Canals   http://www.franceway.com/rives_df/boat.htm
A guide to boating on French canals, from Alsace to Sancerrois.

Grand Canal of China   http://www.chinapage.com/canal.html
The world's oldest and longest canal, apparently. Building began in 486 BC and it's 1,114 miles long. More facts and statistics are on this fascinating website.

Historic Canals of   http://parcscanada.risq.qc.ca/
Quebec   canaux
A well-presented site that introduces the traveller to the six historic canals of Quebec, Canada.

Kiel Canal   http://www.kiel-canal.com
An overview of Germany's Kiel Canal and the surrounding areas.

New York Canals   http://www.canals.state.ny.us
The canal network of and around the greatest city in the world.

Ohio's Historic Canals   http://www.infinet.com/~lstevens/canal
One thousand miles of navigable canals explored by this obvious enthusiast.

Panama Canal   http://www.panamacanal.com
Perhaps the most famous of all canals, the Panama. Tour and transit schedules are listed here, along with details of the boats themselves.

The Houseboating Page   http://www.houseboat.net
Houseboat rentals for a holiday with a difference. An easily navigable guide to the floating hotels of North America.

//STAYING THERE

Starting Points

AccommoData   http://www.accomodata.co.uk
All sorts of accommodation can be found here. An excellent search page lets you look for the perfect place by country. Not the most comprehensive coverage but quality wins out over quantity.

HotelGuide.Com   http://www.hotelguide.com
Now that's what we call comprehensive. An easily searchable directory to help you find a room at more than 60,000 hotels in every conceivable corner of the planet.

AA Hotel Guide http://www.theaa.co.uk/hotels
An interactive, online-bookable version of the famous UK hotel guide.

Alton Towers http://www.alton-towers.co.uk
There's a hotel in Britain's popular theme park with equally themed accommodation – like the chocolate room, with its giant chocolate dispensing machine.

B&B My Guest http://www.beduk.co.uk
An appalling pun but an excellent website featuring 300 bed and breakfast establishments, all with online booking facilities.

Blackpool Hotel Directory http://www.fyldecoast.co.uk
The definitive hotel guide to the famous north-west of England resort known for its amusement park, illuminations – and fearsome landladies.

British Seaside Holiday Hotels http://www.hotellink.co.uk
Roll up your trousers, bring a deckchair and put a hankie on your head as you plan your stay in a great British seaside resort like Clacton, Skegness and Brighton and more.

Country House Hotels http://www.country-house-hotels.com
A well-presented guide to hotels throughout the UK with a touch of class.

Great Breaks by Email http://www.breaks.co.uk
A good idea for the lazy tourist. Fill in the form detailing your particular travel interests, and let hoteliers email you with offers of short breaks and holidays that match your profile.

Stakis Hotels http://www.stakis.co.uk
Part of the Hilton International hotel group. A simple site with two drop-down list boxes, one for information, the other to make a booking. Select a location, a couple of clicks and you've done it.

The Great British Bed   **http://www.kgp-**
and Breakfast   **publishing.co.uk**

More than 600 B&Bs in the UK, with photos of each establishment and full accommodation and price information.

Travel Inn   **http://www.travelinn.co.uk**

A pleasingly uncluttered site presenting the user with a search engine box and an invitation to enter a UK location. Comprehensive hotel descriptions and directions with street maps.

Camping and Caravanning

ABC Camping   **http://www.abccamping.com**

An excellent guide to campsites throughout France, from Alsace to Rhone-Alpes.

Camping France   **http://www.campingfrance.co.uk**

Under canvas or in a caravan – if you want to do it in France then the campsite search and late availability deals are worth a look here.

CaravanParks.Com   **http://www.caravanparks.com**

A directory-style search site for caravan parking that covers Australia, Canada, Germany, Ireland, Netherlands, New Zealand, South Africa, the UK and the USA.

Caravan SiteFinder UK   **http://www.caravan-sitefinder.co.uk**

The unglamorous end of the holiday market, but someone's got to do it. Where to park your touring caravan, and where to buy or rent one of those funny static ones.

Croatian Camping Union   **http://jagor.srce.hr/camping-hr**

A useful guide to the 277 camping sites in Croatia, 90% of which are along the Adriatic coast.

Eurocamp   **http://www.eurocamp.co.uk**

A very colourful website that offers self-drive camping holidays across Europe. One nice touch is the use of 360-degree panoramic views of all the accommodation on offer.

European Camping Index   http://www.oginet.com/camping
Links to camping and caravanning sites across Europe. A good starting point both for newcomers and old hands.

Good Times   http://www.good-times.co.uk
Family camping holidays in Cornwall. Rent-a-tent section has lots about all the different types of tent you can, er, rent.

HAPNZ   http://www.holidayparks.co.nz
The Holiday Accommodation Parks of New Zealand includes details of both caravan and campervan sites.

MyVacationGuide   http://www.myvacationguide.com
A directory of campgrounds and trailer parks for those who love to go a-wandering in Canada.

Ontario Camping Association   http://www.ontcamp.on.ca
Organising camping in Canada since 1933, a guide to accredited camps and a campers search engine make this website good value.

Portugal Camping Guide   http://www.roteiro-campista.pt
Simply click on a picture of a tent, caravan, motor home or whatever takes your fancy to find out more about your Portuguese options.

RV USA   http://www.rvusa.com
Follow the 'campgrounds' link for a directory of places to park up your Recreational Vehicle (that's a caravan to you and me).

Timber Mountain   http://www.timbermountain.com
Camping in the Canadian Rockies. This site tells you what to bring and how to get there.

Tulip Parcs   http://www.hollandtulipparcs.nl
A coalition of 25 Dutch camping sites – use them to plan your tour of Holland.

UK Camping and http://camping.uk-
Caravanning Directory directory.com
The place to go if you are looking for somewhere to pitch your tent. Or buy a caravan and chat with other happy campers.

USA Camp Sites http://www.usacampsites.com
A huge directory of camp sites in the USA, funnily enough. Click on the map and follow the links.

Yogi Bear's Jellystone http://www.frii.com/
Park of Estes ~yogibear/jellystone
A 35-acre campsite located at the gateway to the Rocky Mountain National Park.

House Swaps

International Home http://www.
Exchange Network homexchange.com
Exchange your home with someone else who wants to swap with you. The Internet is ideal for making this kind of global match.

Holi-Swaps http://www.holi-swaps.com
A fairly basic site but with worldwide swaps in 55 countries plus an extensive US selection, looks could be deceiving.

Latitudes Home Exchange http://www.home-swap.com
Offering swaps in 30 countries and a 'custom matching' service to ensure an equal exchange.

Seniors Home http://www.
Exchange seniorshomeexchange.com
Home-swapping holiday service strictly for the over 50s only.

International Hotels

All Hotels http://www.all-hotels.com
Ten thousand or so hotels and lodgings worldwide. OK, so it's

nowhere near all the hotels in the world, but instant online reservation facilities add to the usefulness of an already impressive site.

Ariau Amazon Towers   http://www.ariauamazontowers.com
A unique hotel built entirely at canopy level in the rainforests of Brazil. Check out the honeymoon suite located 110 feet up a mahogany tree!

Double Tree Hotels   http://www.doubletree.com
Double Tree run more than 240 hotels in the USA and Mexico. A search directory and online booking are overshadowed by all-too-brief hotel descriptions.

Featherbed   http://www.
Railroad Company   featherbedrailroad.com
Bed and breakfast accommodation in railway carriages in California, complete with jacuzzi tubs for two.

Hilton Hotels   http://www.hilton.com
Well-organised, easy-to-navigate site with a simple online reservation system.

HotelWorld   http://www.hotelworld.com
A global hotel guide with a simple search facility and very fast real-time quotations and reservations.

LeisureHunt   http://www.leisurehunt.com
Speed is the essence here. A turbocharged hotel-hunting search service, twinned with an equally nimble 'speedbook' service for reservations.

PriceLine   http://www.priceline.com
Name your price for a hotel room and this outfit will see if any of their participating agents will accept it. If they do, you have a bargain. And if you don't, you've only lost a couple of minutes of your time.

Sheraton Hotels   http://www.sheraton.com

All the information you need on every Sheraton hotel and resort around the globe. Oh, and the necessary online reservation system.

Holiday Camps

Camp Beaumont   http://www.campbeaumont.com

The great American summer camp is now available for British kids at various sites in the UK. Full details of all camps, a guide for parents and the essential online booking facility.

Center Parcs   http://www.centerparcs.com

Family-oriented holiday camps under big glass subtropical domes dotted around the British countryside.

Pontins   http://www.pontins.co.uk

Archetypal British holiday camp is now a 'family holiday centre' instead. No online bookings, but you can buy 'Captain Croc' memorabilia if the spirit moves you.

Hostels

Hostels.Com   http://www.hostels.com

A hostel finder that will track down basic accommodation in even the remotest of places.

WorldWide Hostel Guide   http://hostels.com

Thousands of hostels in 150 regions throughout the world.

Youth Hostel Association   http://www.yha.org.uk

Detailed information on the 230 youth hostels throughout the UK. Features a characteristic-based search facility, so you can look for a city hostel or a medium-sized country hostel with equal ease.

1001 Villas http://www.1001-villa-holidaylets.com
A collection of villas to rent around the globe. We didn't count to see if there were exactly 1,001 of them, though.

Chez Nous http://www.cheznous.com
Holiday homes for rent in France. If you are looking for something a little more permanent, they even have some you can buy outright.

Country Retreats http://www.country-retreats.com
Self-catering or B&B accommodation in cottages, farmhouses and manor houses located in the countryside throughout Britain.

Cyber Rentals http://cyberrentals.com
A mighty database of private homes for holiday hire. The focus is on the USA, but there are homes all around the world listed on this easy-to-use site.

Elysian Holidays http://www.elysianholidays.co.uk
Villa rentals around Europe and the Caribbean. A nice site let down slightly by the complex booking process, which involves a combination of email and traditional postal services.

French Life http://www.frenchlife.co.uk
Cottages, villas or camping – take your pick of more than 1,000 properties in some of France's most beautiful regions.

Gites de France http://www.gites.freeserve.co.uk
Excellent self-catering villas in France.

Holiday Bank http://www.holidaybank.co.uk
A searchable online noticeboard of self-catering villa accommodation classified with full descriptions and contact details including email in most cases.

Internet Holiday Rentals   **http://www.holiday-rentals.co.uk**
More than 1,000 private homes around the world that are available for holidaymakers to rent.

Island Hideaways   **http://www.islandhideaways.com**
Caribbean villas, with photographs and descriptions of each property, plus availability and pricing.

Private Villas   **http://www.pvillas.co.uk**
A gateway to privately owned holiday accommodation. Plenty of property listed, but you deal direct with the owner rather than book online.

Spanish Affair   **http://www.spanishaffair.com**
Villas for rent in the Spanish regions of Andalucia, Cantabria and Asturias.

Timeshare

Despite the well-reported scams of the past, timeshares are still sold widely – and for many, they are a good accommodation option. Before you do go any further, you must visit the Timeshare Users Group (http://www.tug2.net) for unbiased opinions and information. If you are still convinced that timeshare is for you – even after reading the section entitled 'Cold Hard Facts About Selling Your Timeshare' – then try these sites:

Timeshares Direct   **http://www.timesharesdirect.com**
A neat, searchable database of timeshares for sale or rent.

TimeShared.Com   **http://www.timeshared.com**
Timeshare sales, trades, purchases and rentals here, organised by country or continent.

Try these Newsgroups

misc.transport.air-industry
Insiders and consumers argue about sky travel.

misc.transport.marine
Boats big and small.

misc.transport.misc
Transportation free-for-all.

misc.transport.rail.americas
Trainspotting USA.

misc.transport.rail.autralia-nz
Trains down under.

misc.transport.rail.europe
Le tunnel and les trains.

misc.transport.rail.misc
Real train obsessives.

misc.transport.road
General road talk.

misc.transport.urban-transit
The tricky problem of getting around in towns.

uk.transport
The tricky problem of getting around Britain.

uk.transport.air
Chocks away!

uk.transport.buses
Ding-ding, hold tight please!

uk.transport.london
Bitter, miserable commuters.

7//TRAVELLING IN STYLE

By now you will have realised that the Internet is an essential tool for the bargain-hunting traveller – so it may come as a surprise that it also serves the opposite end of the travel spectrum equally well. The same flight discounters that do so well in trimming the costs of economy class to the bone can also ease the financial burden of first-class flights and accommodation. The big hotel reservation sites have enough clout to squeeze extra discounts on all rooms, and that includes the best suites in the house.

But maybe ordinary first-class travel isn't quite good enough for that once-in-a-lifetime trip. Go online and you can easily hunt down charter companies that will hire anything from a Cessna to a 747 for your exclusive use. If you want to get the best berth on a long-haul cruise, the websites will reveal full cabin plans in seconds. Or how about letting the train take the strain, in the opulent style of the Orient Express or the even more exclusive Queen of Scots?

If you really have money to burn, why not hire an island for a week or two, book a seat on a space rocket, or take a submarine tour around the wreck of the Titanic? If you want to be truly decadent then let someone else arrange it all for you. See the luxury holidays section for details of companies who are happy to help.

//ADDRESS BOOK

Starting Points

Luxury Link   **http://www.luxurylink.com**
An online travel service dedicated to doing things in style. Luxury yachts, villas, tours and cruises can all be found here.

The Leading Hotels of the World　　　　**http://www.lhw.com**
Choose a destination and then browse comprehensive details of
the top-drawer hotels you can find there – such as the Meurice in
Paris, the Four Seasons in Tokyo or Venice's magnificent Cipriani.

Cars

Aston Martin　　　　**http://www.astonmartin.com**
Forget about car hire: go the whole hog and buy an Aston Martin
Lagonda for the grand tour. All you need to know about the
refined supercar.

Bespokes　　　　**http://www.bespokes.co.uk**
Car hire for the discerning motorist. Classic cars such as Ferrari
Dino, E-Type Jag, Aston Martin Vantage, Porsche 911 Convertible,
Bristol 411 and many more.

Off the Hook　　　　**http://www.offthehookbc.com**
Custom-made tours of British Columbia in a luxury motorhome.
And no, we don't mean a souped-up caravan – more like a top-of-
the-range hotel on wheels, complete with chauffeur, private chef
and tour crew.

Rolls Royce　　　　**http://www.rollsroyceandbentley.co.uk**
A delightful site that is almost as smooth as the cars it is selling. If
you want the ultimate in modern luxury motoring, then a Roller or
Bentley is hard to beat.

Vintage Hire　　　　**http://www.ipta.co.uk/vintage.htm**
Exceptional chauffeur-driven vintage cars, including a 1935 Rolls
Royce limousine. Airport collections, day hire or country touring if
you really want to throw your money around in style.

Flights of Fancy

1st Air
http://www.1st-air.net

Discounted air travel for those wanting to travel first-class. Fly with major airlines at up to 60% off the published first-class fares.

Airborne Adventures
http://www.airborne.co.uk

Hot air balloon flights in the north of England, across the beauty of the Yorkshire Dales. Online booking and full details down to what to wear and how fast you fly.

Concorde
http://www.british-airways.com/concorde

Still the flagship of the British Airways fleet, Concorde is starting to show its age now. However, there is nothing to beat whizzing across the Atlantic on the world's only supersonic aircraft.

Flight Fantasy
http://www.flightfantasy.com

Want to hire a 747? No problem for Flight Fantasy, who promise that no request is too outrageous. Private aircraft charter is a speciality, and when they say first class, they mean it – as the images on this website show.

First Heli Network
http://www.first-heli-network.co.uk

Helicopters for sale if you have the odd US$4 million or so wasting away doing nothing. When we visited, there was also a Boeing 737 aeroplane on offer for just US$9.75 million, or near offer...

Lear Jet
http://www.learjet.com

If you need to ask the price then you definitely cannot afford a Lear jet. Still, the Bombardier Aerospace website makes for interesting drooling.

Mighty MiG Bulletin Board
http://www.barnstormers.com/ABC/ABC9900/mig9900.html

If money is no object, why not buy your own MiG jet fighter? No, we are not kidding. This is a bulletin board dedicated to people buying and selling whole MiGs as well as parts and supplies for them.

Luxury Trains

Blue Train   http://www.bluetrain.co.za
Top-notch train travel on a state-owned railway service. The Blue Train travels between Cape Town and Pretoria in air-conditioned, carpeted and cosseted comfort. The website has all the facts and fares.

Great South Pacific Express   http://www.gspe.com/index.html
A joint venture between Queensland Rail and Venice Simplon has produced this Australian Orient Express. Itineraries and travel information can be found at the appropriately refined website.

Indian Pacific   http://www.gsr.com.au/theindianpacific
The last true trans-continental train journey remaining in the world today. Traverse Australia coast to coast, from Perth to Sydney via Adelaide, in the splendid comfort of first class.

Northern Sky   http://www.northernsky.com
Private rail cruises on any Amtrak route. These luxury carriages – complete with four double staterooms, kitchen and home cinema entertainment systems – are simply hooked up to an Amtrak train.

Orient Express Trains   http://www.orient-express.com
Trains don't come any classier than this: the Venice Simplon Orient Express, the British Pullman, the Great South Pacific Express. All the itineraries plus online booking.

Palace on   http://www.rajasthan-
Wheels   tourism.com/rajtourism/pow.htm
A luxurious train that conjures up the opulent world of the maharajas as you travel through the Rajasthan desert in India.

Queen of Scots　　　　　　http://www.queenofscots.co.uk
Quite possibly the most exclusive of the luxury trains still running in the UK, and maybe even the world.

Rovos Rail　　　　　　http://www.bookorbuy.com/rovos
How about a steam train safari through the heart of Africa for something classy and different? For real luxury you will be wanting a Royal Suite, each of which takes up half a carriage.

Cruising

Elite Yacht Charters　　　　　　http://www.eliteyacht.com
Fancy hiring a massive 300-footer – if your wallet can stretch that far? Whatever your taste, Elite have the right charter for you.

Loch Ness Charters　　　　　　http://lochness-charters.com
Yacht and cruiser charters in the Loch Ness, Great Glen and Caledonian Canal areas of Scotland. They cannot guarantee you will spot Nessie herself, though.

QE2　　　　　　http://www.cunardline.com
The legendary cruiser still sails regularly between Southampton and New York. It's posh, all right – there is one crew member to every two passengers.

Virgin Traders　　　　　　http://www.virgin-traders.com
Motor-yacht charter in the beauty of the British Virgin Islands, plus big-game fishing if you want. One look at the picture on the home page and you will be hooked yourself.

Yacht Charters　　　　　　http://www.travelsource.com/yachts
A selection of luxury charters, including a 72-foot sailing yacht in the British Virgin Islands.

Luxury Holidays

Abercrombie and Kent http://www.travelvoyager.com/abercrombie

Privately organised safaris, luxury train travel, exclusive beach resorts. Tour operators specialising in extravagant services to discerning clients.

Castle Stuart http://www.castlestuart.com

The entire eight-bedroom, seventeenth-century Scottish 'Tower House', complete with ghost and full Highland breakfast, for £1,200 a night.

France in Your Glass http://www.inyourglass.com

If you like a little vino, why not combine fine wines from private vineyards in France with luxury travel and accommodation? Sounds like a jolly nice idea to us. Hic!

Go Wild Luxury Safaris http://www.info.bw/~go.wild/luxury.htm

The call of the African wild. And steaming hot showers, proper loos, chilled champagne and gourmet grub every evening.

Grand Wailea Resort, Maui, Hawaii http://www.grandwailea.com

Forty acres of prime beachfront property featuring a 'five diamond'-rated hotel with suites of up to 5,000 square feet, a world-class health spa and a championship golf course.

In The Wake of Lewis & Clark http://www.expeditions.com

A 1,200-mile journey along the path of the Columbia River in a top-notch expedition ship.

Luxury Link Auctions http://www.luxurylink.com

Just because you've got the money doesn't mean you can't have some fun saving a little. Luxury holidays are auctioned off on this site, with something new every week.

One + One **http://www.grand-adventure.com**

Holidays in Thailand, including the grand elephant safari. Need we point out that this means riding them rather than shooting them?

Pakatoa Island **http://www.**
Resort **hauraki.com/pakatoa/index.html**

A privately owned paradise in New Zealand, 25 nautical miles from Auckland. New Zealand's only true island resort.

Serious money

If you are stuck for ideas but loaded with cash, you could do a lot worse than try the 'Serious Money' section at renowned bargain site LastMinute (**http://www. lastminute.com**). A trip to the edge of space in a MiG fighter jet is £9,000; a jaunt on one of the world's fastest motor yachts just £7,750. We liked the sound of 'No Mans Land' – a refurbished seafort located off Portsmouth, in southwest England. The price of £31,000 for a day includes helicopter transfers and a maximum of 100 guests.

Scottish Castle **http://www.**
Tours **castles.org/Chatelaine/tours.htm**

Guided tours of Scottish castles, made to measure or off the peg – you choose.

Swim With Dolphins **http://www.dolphinworld.org**

A trip to the Florida Keys to swim with dolphins for 30 minutes. Or swim with a trainer as well, in which case get your feet kissed and a dorsal fin ride – from the dolphin, not the trainer.

TCS Expeditions **http://www.tcs-expeditions.com**

Specialising in world exploration with a bit of class. Small touches like flying in a privately owned all-first-class Boeing 757 or a luxury private train, for example.

Uncommon Journeys   **http://uncommonjourneys.com**
Specialising in luxury train and ocean travel, Uncommon Journeys present their itinerary on this website. The QE2 transatlantic crossing and a cruise around Hawaii being representative of what's on offer.

World Health Spa Directory   **http://www.worldhealthspa.com**
More than 1,000 health spas listed. The perfect way to get a little luxury, while telling everyone else that it's all for the good of your body and soul.

Once-in-a-Lifetime Experiences

Deep Sea Voyages   **http://www.deepseavoyages.com**
From underwater tours of the volcanoes in the Azores to the ultimate tourist trip – a submarine tour of the Titanic.

Necker Island   **http://www.neckerisland.com**
You can hire Richard Branson's paradise island at the north-eastern extreme of the British Virgin Islands, along with a staff of 31 to pamper you, for as little as £8,000 per day (rising to £14,000 depending on number of guests).

Zegrahm Space Voyages   **http://www.spacevoyages.com**
With trips to space scheduled to start in July 2002, these guys are not kidding. If you have the desire and the dosh (at least US$50,000 by the look of it) you can blast off for the ultimate adventure holiday.

Hotels

Grand Hyatt, New York   **http://www.new-york.hyatt.com**
On Park Avenue, right next to Grand Central Station, a hotel of epic proportions. Some 1,347 rooms and 54 suites are available, and five-star service is standard to them all.

Hotel Jerome, Aspen, Colorado   http://www.hoteljerome.com
The ski resort to be seen in, and a decent little hotel to stay in. The
Grand Parlour Suite, for example, offers 1,200 square feet of luxury
– including a butler's pantry.

Sandals Royal   http://www.sandals.com/main/
Caribbean   royal/entry-rj-home.html
A hotel on the only private offshore island in Jamaica, complete with
four gourmet restaurants, four swimming pools and a golf club.

Shiv Niwas Palace,   http://www.
Rajasthan   hrhindia.com/shiv.html
Adjoining the home of the Maharaja of Udaipur, this really is a
palace hotel. Enormous suites with huge chandeliers and gigantic
marble bathrooms are the norm.

Small Luxury Hotels of the World   http://www.slh.com/slh
From The Ritz in London to Raffles in Singapore – find them all in
this small luxurious website.

The Mena House   http://www.
Oberoi, Cairo   oberoihotels.com/mena.htm
Forty acres of jasmine-scented gardens, an 18-hole golf course, 804
beds and all literally in the shadows of the pyramids. Online
bookings available, of course.

The Oriental,   http://www.mandarin-
Bangkok   oriental.com/bangkok
120 years of colonial elegance and history, and one of the few
remaining true grand hotels in the world. A staff of well over 1,000
serves 396 sumptuous rooms.

The Palace of the Lost City,   http://www.sun-
Sun City   international.com
The Lost City is an African fantasy world for the rich and famous,
bringing the glitz of Las Vegas to South Africa. Sun City is famous

for its entertainment and casinos – and now for this extraordinary hotel as well.

The Park Lane Hotel, Hong Kong   http://www.parklane.com.hk
An affordable bit of luxury at one of Hong Kong's finest hotels, a towering structure that offers fantastic views of both Victoria Park and the harbour.

Turtle Island, Fiji   http://www.turtlefiji.com
A five-star resort island that covers 500 acres of paradise, yet houses only fourteen couples at any time. A virtual tour is available on the website. Just as well, as most of us will never be able to afford the real thing.

Waipo Tree House   http://www.waipo.com
OK, we grant you a tree house doesn't sound that luxurious. But when it is located in a giant monkeypod tree in Hawaii, overlooking a 2,000-foot waterfall, you start to get the idea.

Waldorf Astoria,   http://www.hilton.com/
New York   hotels/NYCWAHH
The website lets you take a video tour of what is perhaps America's best-known luxury hotel -- and one with 100 years of history behind it.

World Executive   http://www.
Hotel Directory   worldexecutive.com
Astonishingly speedy and easy to use. A directory takes you to some of the best hotels on the planet. Once you find the right one, a room can be reserved within minutes.

London Luxury

The UK *capital is well blessed with high-class hotels. The names are familiar throughout the western world, and often beyond. Here is our brief website guide to the crème de la crème of rented rooms.*

Brown's
http://accessworldwide.com/
wwhr/lemeridien/browns

London's oldest five-star hotel, operating right in the heart of Mayfair since 1837. Shame the website isn't as inspiring, though.

Claridges
http://www.savoy-group.co.uk/
master/html/cla1.htm

Claridges in Mayfair is famous for both its art deco restaurant and level of service. For example, each room has waiter, maid and valet call buttons.

Grosvenor House
http://www.grosvenorhouse.co.uk/gh

Known as London's best address, Grosvenor House is located slap-bang on Park Lane in the heart of Mayfair.

The Lanesborough
http://www.lanesborough.com

Heads of state and celebrity guests use the Royal Suite here. Three bedrooms, a drawing and dining room, kitchen, personal butler, 24-hour security and a chauffeur-driven limo.

The Savoy
http://www.savoy-group.co.uk/
master/html/savoy1.htm

If you want to stay in a two-bedroom river-view suite, you had better have at least £1,500 a night to spare.

8//THE SEASONED TRAVELLER

'Cyber café' is the mildly tedious name for a remarkably traveller-friendly resource – a place where you can hang out, log on and maybe ingest a cup of good chai in the bargain. A couple of years ago, if you were hitching your way across some foreign backwater and wanted to keep in touch with the folks back home, your options were pretty limited. You might have been able to send an intermittent postcard, but chances were good that you would reach home sweet home before it did. You even might have been able to make the odd phone call, but your voice would break up almost as fast as the cash in your wallet. And even finding a phone was problematic. Nowadays, 'phone shops' have become ubiquitous. The author, for example, bumped into one in a ramshackle village in the heart of Kenyan safari land recently. What's more, like many of these outposts, the phone shop also provided Internet access. Phone shops (your best bet in more remote areas) tend to be well advertised – usually the marketing takes the form of garish signs for miles around. It is equally impossible to miss the 'true' cyber cafés that have sprung up in almost every big city on the planet. Not only are the signs just as garish, they are also in English.

Of course, once inside the friendly local cyber café, you don't want to spend ages trying to configure foreign software. By far the easiest method of keeping your email up and running while abroad is to set up a web-based email service before you take off (see page 16). The likes of HotMail, Netscape WebMail and Yahoo! Mail are all well recognised now. Setting up an account costs nothing, and involves no more than spending ten minutes filling in online forms and configuring your account once it's up and running. After that, the world of email is your oyster, no matter which sea you happen to be swimming in.

Picture postcards too tacky? Why not make the most of technology and send an electronic postcard instead? There are plenty of websites that let you do just this, ranging from a simple snapshot to customisable cards with greetings and even multimedia fripperies. And since you're already in computer communication mode, why not join in topical discussion on the Usenet Newsgroup system, or get chatting to other travellers using Internet Relay Chat? One of the things you may find yourself talking about is where to eat. Bad food or drink ruins a trip quicker than bad company. Knowing where and what to eat is essential if you are to enjoy your trip – and this is where the vast array of restaurant guides online come in handy. Find the right sites for your journey by using a search engine to look for a combination of 'food' or 'restaurant' with the location concerned.

PCs have been slowly but surely shrinking in size at much the same rate as they have been increasing in power, so you might want to take yours with you. The days of the 'luggable' computer have gone, replaced by notebooks, sub-notebooks and palmtop devices that you can easily take with you on your travels. However, like the proverbial boy scout, you must be prepared. While most new models have dual voltage, they don't come with the various plugs needed to cope with foreign wall sockets. And your brand-new built-in modem probably won't connect to the telephone sockets of exotic climes, either.

//ADDRESS BOOK

Starting Points

Some websites are so knowledge-rich that they should be mandatory bookmarks in every traveller's browser. Some are best described as 'the whole package' and act as essential guides for the independent traveller, while others are much tighter in their focus.

Lonely Planet   http://www.lonelyplanet.com

Maps and facts and fun from this polished, yet plain-speaking, magazine-style site. The print versions of these Lonely Planet Guides have become essential items for many a traveller.

Rec.Travel Library   http://www.travel-library.com

A superbly indexed library of links to travel information that proves invaluable for quickly finding even the quirkiest of facts about any given destination.

Rough Guides to Travel   http://travel.roughguides.com

Rough Guides really need little introduction. The website brings interactivity, added value and immediacy. Not to be missed.

The Virtual Tourist   http://www.vtourist.com

Very real tourists from all around the world share their experiences. If you want the real truth about travelling, look no further.

Mobile Computing

Connect Globally   http://www.connectglobally.com

These guys will help you make sure your PC works in foreign countries, with phone, modem and electrical kits.

Laptop Travel   http://www.laptoptravel.com

Kit for your travelling laptop, plus travellers' tips submitted by customers.

Roadnews http://www.roadnews.com

Devoted to the traveller with a laptop. Holidaymaker and salesman alike, this site provides answers to your mobile computing problems.

TeleAdapt http://www.teleadapt.com

Specialising in simple and cost-effective travel kits, TravelAdapt can solve many a connection problem.

Keeping in Touch

To introduce you to the world of the cyber café, take a look at these sites. We've listed the real-world addresses should you be in the area, but you can visit them all on the web without leaving home.

Cyber Cafés

The Internet Café Guide http://www.netcafeguide.

Exemplary site tells you how cyber cafés actually work, and supply a directory to the location of thousands of them around the world.

Alaska

Fairnet http://www.fairnet.org

1512 Cowles Street, Fairbanks, Alaska USA

Aruba (Lesser Antilles)

Café Internet http://www.cybercafe.aw

Suite 204, Royal Plaza Mall, LG Smith Blvd, Oranjestad, Aruba

California

Cyberjava http://www.cyberjava.com

7080 Hollywood Blvd, Hollywood.

Jeremy's Cyber Café and http://www.
Beer Haus joshua-tree.com/jeremys

61597, 29 Palms Highway, Joshua Tree.

@Coffee http://www.atcoffee.com
7200 Melrose Ave, Los Angeles.

The Coffeenet http://www.coffeenet.net
744 Harrison Street, San Francisco.

Chile

La Torre Suiza http://www.torresuiza.com
969 Fco, Bilbao, Villarrica

China

Mark's Internet http://www.
Center markguide.com/english/index.htm
19 Guangming Road, Urumqi, Xinjiiang

London

Cyberia http://www.cyberiacafe.net
39 Whitfield Street, London W1P 5RE

If you know your itinerary, take a look at the websites of any cyber cafés you might be using to check out the exact facilities on offer. If you have any precise queries, email the owner and ask.

Nepal

Easylink Cyber Café http://www.visitnepal.com/easylink
Thamel, Kathmandu, Bagmati Zone

New Zealand

NetCentral http://www.netcentral.co.nz
5 Lorne Street, Auckland Central.

Cyber Café http://www.cybercafe-chch.co.nz
Shop 1,2,3 Gloucester Arcade, 127 Gloucester Street, Christchurch.

Russia

Vyatka Intercom http://www.inetcafe.vyatka.ru
67 Svobody Street, Kirov

Tanzania

CyberSpot http://www.cyberspot.co.tz
Jamhuri Street, Dar es Salaam

Thailand

Hilltribe Internet http://members.tripod.com/
Cyber Kitchen ~cyberkitchen/index.htm
360 Moo 3, Ban Pasang, Mae Chan 57710, Chiang Rai

Web-Based Chat and Discussion Forums

For a full list of Usenet newsgroups, try the searchable directory of newsgroups at the Usenet Info Center Launch Pad (http:// metalab.unc.edu/usenet-I). Web-based chat forums are a relatively new idea and as such can be a bit hit-and-miss. A well-designed website forum will be easy to use, responsive and will thread messages so you can follow conversations. Many travel-related websites carry such forums for user feedback.

Webarrow http://webarrow.net/chatindex
A directory of web chat services that also lists the top 50 chat sites.

Web-Based Email

AltaVista Mail http://altavista.iname.com
Offers unique email addresses such as @mail.com or @doctor.com

HotMail http://www.hotmail.com
Now owned by Microsoft and the biggest of the web-based free email services, with more than 10 million users.

Juno   http://www.juno.com
A user-friendly graphical interface to access your email.

Lycos Email   http://www.lycosemail.com
Add chat and message boards into the mix and Lycos Email becomes an all-in-one communications centre for the traveller.

Netscape WebMail   http://webmail.netscape.com
An email address for life, accessed using the web, from one of the best-known names on the Internet.

Yahoo! Mail   http://mail.yahoo.com
Combine it with the Yahoo! Messenger service and get instant notification of new mail as it arrives.

Postcards

All Yours Digital   http://www.all-
Postcards   yours.net/postcard/dp.html
1,000 pictures to choose from, plus options to add background music and customised text.

Just Postcards   http://www.justpostcards.com
A huge selection of customisable postcards categorised by subject matter. A free service with a highly graphic yet simple-to-use interface.

Postcards From   http://www.
The Web   homearts.com/postcard/00postf1.htm
Not too many categories to choose from, but most cards are animated for additional effect.

The Insider's Guide

These sites offer the kind of insider knowledge that can only be gained by actually going somewhere. They're written and published by professional backpackers, world travellers and other travellers, linked by a passion for travel and a desire to share knowledge – and have the kind of information that's taken years to garner. Whether you want to know how to doss down at airports and save money on accommodation or where the best place to eat in a foreign land is, you'll find it here.

1000 Travel Tips   http://www.1000traveltips.org
Aimed at hardcore backpacker types who want to visit places avoided by most tourists. A goldmine of information for anyone infected with severe wanderlust.

Betty's Travel Kiosk   http://www.afn.org/~afn11300
Based on Betty's own travels to all continents, this site is full of photographs and personal experiences.

British Scareways   http://www.aviation-uk.com
If you really want to know about near misses and aircraft safety, this is interesting and frightening reading.

Budget Traveller's Guide   http://www3.sympatico.ca/
to Sleeping in Airports   donna.mcsherry/airports.htm
Many airports are more comfortable than local lodgings, and much cheaper. This site reviews which are best and which should be avoided.

Completely Unofficial   http://www.thomson-holidays.
Thomson Holiday Real Feedback   freeserve.co.uk
A long-winded name, but one that sums this site up perfectly. Customers of the big British tour operator tell it like it was, good or bad.

EarthWatch   http://www.earthwatch.com
Fascinating stuff: 3D weather information and forecasting for the USA, plus Atlantic and Pacific satellite images.

Festpass   http://www.festpass.com
A guide to European music and arts festivals with a database of

more than 1,300 festival details to search through. From the Finnish wife-carrying world championships to the no-sex-before-marriage art festival (Czech Republic), there's bound to be something to tickle your festive fancy.

Footloose Net   http://www.footloose.net
A community of travel forums, organised by destination and travel type, where you can share your experiences with other travellers.

How Far Is It?   http://www.indo.com/distance
Type in any two places, and this simple yet ingenious site will tell you how far apart they are.

How to See the World   http://www.artoftravel.com
Subtitled 'The Art of European and World Travel Backpacking on $25 a Day or Less' this free online text is something every money-conscious traveller should read.

JourneyWoman   http://www.journeywoman.com
An online travel magazine just for the girlies. Includes items such as 'What should I wear, where?' but also less stereotyped features like '100 female travel tips from around the world', including a special selection for the 'older adventuress'.

Lorry Patton's Travel   http://www.
Tips 'n' Tricks   lorrypatton.com
Lots of things you really need to know before you set off.

PassengerRights.Com   http://www.passengerrights.com
Power to the people. If you want to complain about a travel experience that went bad, fill in an online complaint form and then choose who to email from the directory of official avenues in airlines, holiday companies and the like

Roadside America   http://www.roadsideamerica.com
Offbeat tourist attractions scattered throughout the USA. Don't miss the Terror of Pelican Rapids, or the Road Cheese Hypertour.

Round The World   http://www.travel-
Travel Guide   library.com/rtw/html

Not a fancy website, but a useful one: an online guide to the
ultimate trip, the full circle around the world.

Sensational Sabbatical   http://www.omni.cc.purdue.edu/
Suggestions   ~alltson/sabbat.htm

Things to do with a long leave of absence, if you're lucky enough
to get one.

Shoestring Travel   http://www.stratpub.com

Cheapo hints collected by email and from Usenet, helpfully
regurgitated for like-minded penny-pinching travellers. Nice!

Solo Travel   http://www.travel-
Network   wise.com/solo/index1.html

There are those brave souls who prefer to travel alone, but not to
travel lonely. This is for them.

Tips 4 Trips   http://www.tips4trips.com

A site stuffed full of tips by and for the international traveller –
everything you can imagine is covered here, from travelling with
pets to tips for the disabled traveller.

Travel at the   http://vanbc.
Speed of Light   wimsey.com/~ayoung/travel.shtml

On the edge and off the wall. True travel stories from people
who've been there, done that and got the T-shirt.

TravelMag   http://www.travelmag.co.uk

A guide to independent travel, from riding Harley Davidsons
across South Africa to driving from London to Australia with a baby
in the back.

Universal Currency Converter   http://www.xe.net/ucc

Money for nothing. Conversion between 180 currencies from 250
countries – it won't cost you anything to use.

US Customs Travellers   http://www.
Information   customs.ustreas.gov/travel
Can you take your pet scorpion to South Dakota? Can you transport sequoia seeds back to Sheffield? The official guide from the people who really know.

Women Travelling   http://www.
Together   women-traveling.com
Men. Who needs 'em? An organisation that helps single women travellers locate other female travel partners.

World Tour of   http://www.
Beaches   oneweb.com/infoctrs/beaches.html
For lazy days by the sea, here's in-depth info about the world's beaches. Don't forget the sun cream.

Eating Out

Ant's Top   http://web.bham.ac.uk/
112 UK Pubs   ggy4atv3/goodpubs
It's a tough job, but some lucky so-and-so has decided to do it. The number in the title will almost certainly change as Ant anonymously visits more pubs and inspects their facilities.

Dine.Com   http://www.dine.com
It's not just burgers and fries. The top 125,000 restaurants in the USA.

Eat Germany   http://www.eat-germany.net/
With typical Germanic attention to detail, this site has a complex search engine that lets you specify the tiniest detail – such as how much you want to spend or places with outside seating.

Gastronomy   http://www.parisfranceguide.com/
France   gastronomy/gastronomy.htm
A virtual tour of French food and drink. Pick a region and pig out on the information.

Global Gourmet   http://www.globalgourmet.com/destinations
Select a destination and click on the link to reveal recipes associated with that country. You could try Grandma's Easter Cheese from Poland on a slice of Ethiopian Honey Yeast Bread.

Sheldon Landwehr's   http://www.
International Restaurant Guide   sheldonlandwehr.com
Restaurant reviews from the New York Post food critic. As Landwehr says, 'Sacred cows are not respected' – and he kicks ass where deserved.

Tokyo Food Page   http://www.bento.com/l1-1.html
Where to buy fresh octopus tentacles in Tokyo. Fortunately, it also points you in the right direction for eating and drinking around town.

Ultimate Restaurant   http://www.
Directory   orbweavers.com/ultimate
Select a cuisine from the extensive list and then choose a country. Out pops a restaurant or restaurants to match. Mmm.

Wines on the Internet   http://www.wines.com/wines.html
A guide to wines and wineries that will appeal to hobbyists, experts and plain-old plonk-drinking tourists alike.

Backpacker Bonding

Maybe it's something to do with the Internet's academic history and the fact that students around the world get website access through their university or college. Whatever, backpacking is big online.

Art of Travel   http://www.artoftravel.com
A simple backpacker's guide to travel and travel guide books.

Backpacker   http://www.
Essentials   backpackeressentials.com.au

A budget traveller's guide to the world. Written by Australians, but of interest to all.

Backpack Europe   http://www.backpackeurope.com
Travel tips, tales and other interesting stuff.

Backpackers Index   http://www.ozemail.com.au/~backpack
Indexed by country, providing links to all those small travel companies and tour guides you'd never find otherwise. And with a live chat room, too.

Backpacker Magazine   http://www.bpbasecamp.com
The essential inside info for the serious backpacker, including reviews of water bladders and understanding microclimates.

Backpacker Network   http://www.thebackpacker.net
Lots of useful information, including the essential 'beer index'.

Great Outdoors   http://www.greatoutdoors.com
All the equipment you need for various outdoor activities, including an auction of gear.

Worldly Backpacking   http://www.
Pages   esidle.com/travel/travel.html
A treasure trove of information about youth hostels, backpacking economics and travelogues by people in the know.

Try these Newsgroups

---

alt.travel
The daddy of all travel newsgroups.

alt.travel.canada
Where you will always find your man.

alt.travel.marketplace
Psst. Wanna buy a holiday?

alt.travel.ideas
Perfect for brainstorming.

alt.travel.road.trip
The hitchhiker's guide to travel.

rec.travel.budget.backpack
Budget travel discussion, not cheap handbags.

rec.travel.misc
Assorted travel-related waffle.

//FAQS – FREQUENTLY ASKED QUESTIONS

//USING THE INTERNET

Q What do I need to get started on the net?

A You need a PC, modem, telephone line, an account with an Internet Service Provider (ISP) and some Internet software. The modem plugs into the PC at one end and the telephone socket at the other. This is then used to dial into a modem at your ISP, which has its computers connected directly to the Internet. The software lets you browse the web, send and receive email and take part in online chats. For more on this, see The Virgin Guide to the Internet.

Q Can I use the Internet without having to buy a computer?

A Yes. If you want only occasional access to the Internet to collect email and research your travel plans then you can make use of an Internet caf or suitably equipped library. These places usually charge you by the hour, but will give infrequent users all the help and advice they need – and they are much cheaper and easier than buying and setting up a PC of your own.

Q Can I have more than one email address?

A Yes, and many people do. If you have an account with an ISP, you'll get at least one email address, but travellers who want to keep in touch while they're away often use one of the free web-based services so that they can pick up their email wherever they are. See page 16 for more details.

Q How much will it cost me to access the Internet from home?

A That depends on how much you pay for an ISP account (often free) and how long you spend online. In the UK, off-peak local calls at the weekend cost 1p per minute; calls at other times cost a lot more.

Q **When does the Internet run at its fastest?**
A This depends on which country you are connecting from and in which country the website you are connecting to is situated. In general, however, when the USA wakes up, the web slows down – that's because most web users are in America.

Q **Do search engine sites index every travel website on the Internet?**
A No. Even the biggest of search sites cannot hope to index more than 20% of the total number of pages out there on the web. To make sure that you aren't missing a good website by using the 'wrong' search engine, use a metasearch engine to perform simultaneous searches at multiple search sites. See page 41 for more about this.

//USING THE WEB

Q **Which is the better browser, Microsoft Internet Explorer or Netscape Navigator?**
A Both browsers have their fans, but there isn't really much to choose between them. They both do the same thing in a similar way. Your ISP will supply you with one or the other, and most people are happy with what they're given. You can, on the other hand, install both and see which you like best – either download them from the Internet or load them from a CD, like the ones given away with the glossy computer magazines.

Q **What are plug-ins?**
A They're little pieces of software that 'plug in' to your web browser and work with it to enable it to do more. Common examples are Shockwave Flash for multimedia presentations and RealPlayer for audio and video displays. See page 7 for more about plug-ins.

Q **The website promised a virtual reality tour of the resort, but** all I got was an empty window in the middle of my browser. What did I do wrong?

A You didn't have the right plug-in. Go back to the site and read the instructions – there should be a link for you to follow to download and install the correct player.

Q **Recently I visited a site that said I needed to accept cookies and wouldn't let me go any further. What gives?**

A You've set your browser not to accept cookies, which are small files that are used by the website to store your personal information such as site username and password, plus any layouts and custom configurations you may have opted for. There's very little reason why you shouldn't accept them – they are generally useful and are used whenever you buy anything from an e-commerce site, so you may wish to change your browser settings to allow them. You can read much more about cookies at http://www.cookiecentral.com.

Q **How on earth am I meant to remember all the different website addresses I visit?**

A You aren't – your browser can do it for you. Use the drop-down menu or a right-click to add your current page to the list of 'bookmarks' or 'favorites'. All the addresses get stored in an indexed directory of URLs. When you want to revisit a site, you just choose the right bookmark. You can give these addresses new names and set up folders to make finding bookmarks easier.

Q **Are there any country-specific search engines that will provide a more local flavour to my searches, or are they all global in nature?**

A Yahoo! has launched a whole host of regional sites, each with country-specific content. There's a list of these on page 56. You can also find country-specific search engines and directories (like 123 India at http://www.123india.com) by using your regular search site

– try entering the name of the country or region and '+"search engine"'.

Q Why do I get error messages every time I try to connect?

A There are three common reasons for this. First, you could be typing in an incorrect address, so check what's in the address bar very carefully; second, the website could be very busy or temporarily out of order, in which case try again later; finally, the website may have closed down or moved to a new location. Try looking for its name using a search engine to see if an alternative address can be found.

Q Can I read the content of web pages without actually being connected to the Internet?

A Yes. You can use the 'offline' feature of your browser, which will store the pages on your hard disk and then load them from this data cache on demand without the need for a further connection. Or you can buy special offline reader software that downloads entire websites you can access via your browser.

//USENET NEWSGROUPS

For lots more on newsgroups, see the companion Virgin Guide to the Internet.

Q How do I 'subscribe' to a newsgroup?

A Just start the newsreader function of your email software (see page 11) to display a listing of all the newsgroups that are available through your ISP. As this list is often well in excess of 15,000 groups, you should use the search or filter facilities to hunt down the one you want by subject matter. Once you've found it, just hit the 'subscribe' button and any new messages will be displayed.

Q Can I search Usenet for postings on specific travel topics without having to join every likely newsgroup and trawl through the messages one by one?

A Yes. Some search engine sites let you search Usenet specifically, or you can go to a specialist Usenet search engine like Deja (**http://www.deja.com**), which keeps huge archives of Usenet postings and lets you search through the lot in just a few seconds.

Q **The message I posted just a few days ago has totally vanished from the newsgroup. What has happened to it?**
A It's expired – been deleted. The sheer volume of messages posted means that your ISP has to delete the archives every few days to prevent their storage disks from filling up.

Q **Since I posted a few messages to a newsgroup I have started getting lots of junk email. Is this a coincidence?**
A No. Some advertisers trawl the newsgroups looking for email addresses, or use special software to rip the addresses out of messages automatically. This junk mail or 'spam' is a real bore – try using a false name when you post messages to newsgroups. Lots of people do.

//SECURITY MATTERS

Q **How safe are my credit card details when sent across the Internet?**
A Providing the website in question is using a secure server (indicated by a little closed padlock in your browser), they're very safe. The secure server ensures that the card details are scrambled using military-strength encryption codes so that no snoopers can intercept them en route.

Q **If the travel agency I want to buy from doesn't have a secure server facility, what should I do?**
A Either find a more professional company that does have secure servers, or place your booking by telephone.

Q **The website claimed to have secure shopping facilities but, when I clicked on the link for the checkout to book my holiday,**

the padlock symbol on my browser remained open. Did I do the right thing by cancelling the transaction?

A Yes, you did. If the padlock doesn't close, then the website remains insecure and you should never give your credit card details out to a site that doesn't have a secure server up and running.

Q **How do I know that the website I'm dealing with isn't going to rip me off?**

A You don't. You must make a judgement call based on common sense. If a deal looks too good to be true, then it usually is. Avoid doing business with any website that looks like it was knocked up in five minutes and has no telephone number or postal contact details. Look out for services that belong to industry bodies such as ABTA, so that if something does go wrong you can get compensation of some kind.

Q **I was about to submit a request for a holiday brochure when a warning box popped up on my screen that said, 'You are about to send information to an insecure site, do you wish to continue?' What should I do?**

A If all you were sending was your email or home address, then it is perfectly OK to carry on – it just means that your web browser security settings have been configured to be particularly tough. However, if you were sending credit card details, they would not have been going to a secure server, so the advice then would be to decline.

Q **I wanted to book a safari with an online company based in Kenya. However, when I tried phoning the contact telephone number, I couldn't get through. What should I do?**

A Find another safari company – there are plenty of them on the web. It could be an innocent mistake, a slip of the keyboard when entering the number on the page, but it could also be an early warning sign that all is not well.

Q **Do I have any rights as a consumer if something should go wrong with an online holiday booking?**

A Yes, of course you do, just as if you were in a shop. However, you should ensure that you read the terms and conditions of booking, including the small print, before you part with any cash.

Q **What if I change my mind about a booking – can I get my money back?**

A As with most travel agents, there is usually a penalty fee, the severity of which depends on how close to departure you cancel. Once again, check the terms and conditions before you pay up.

//ONLINE TRAVEL BOOKING

Q **I don't understand how a website can guarantee that the seat I am booking on a plane is really available. What happens if someone else on the Internet also buys that ticket?**

A That can't happen. The website services use exactly the same flight booking databases that your high-street travel agent uses. These update in real time and will only sell available tickets at the going rate. If someone else buys a ticket on the same plane, the database is updated immediately.

Q **So why should I bother visiting lots of websites and comparing prices if they all use the same databases anyway?**

A Because they all have different deals and can therefore provide the customer with varying discounts. One online service may be able to undercut another on one airline, and vice versa. Comparing lots of sites is the only way to be certain that you've got the best price on offer.

Q **Can I really book flights and reserve hotel rooms at any time of the day or night online?**

A Yes. The Internet never shuts down.

Q **Can I reserve a specific seat on a flight – or do I have to leave it up to the check-in clerk?**
A Some online flight brokers have seat booking systems in place for certain airlines. These allow you to view a plan of the aircraft and click on the seat you'd like to reserve. This service isn't available at all sites and applies to participating airlines only – so check the flight booking sites for details.

Q **Should I buy my flights direct from an airline's online site, or is it better to use a flight broker service?**
A Again there is no simple answer to this one. The no-frills airlines tend to offer the best deals direct from their own websites. However, scheduled airline fares can be greatly discounted if you are buying through a broker. Check both options and see which comes up cheapest.

//MISCELLANEOUS

Q **Can I book a holiday through an online travel agency that is actually based in a foreign country?**
A Yes, although you will need to check with the agent concerned to ensure that they are able to accept foreign bookings. If the agent is based in the USA and their holidays all start out of US airports, then they are of little use to you if you live in Birmingham. Be aware that payment will be made in the foreign currency, so do your conversion calculations carefully to work out exactly whether it really is worth while.

Q **When researching my destination, should I visit unofficial personal pages, or should I stick to official tourist board sites?**
A Do both. Official sites tend to be feature-packed and have lots of detail about accommodation and transportation, while the personal sites can offer a unique insight into local culture and tell you much more about what it's really like.

***Q* I'm not sure where I'm going is safe. How can I check?**
A Use the Internet to find the official statements by British and American governments, which will tell you all you need to know. You can also request to be joined to a mailing list that will keep you informed of all the latest travel advice by email. For more details, see page 14.

//GLOSSARY

applet A small program downloaded from a website on to your PC, from where it is run. However, it appears to be running on the web page itself. See Java.

article A message posted to a Usenet newsgroup. A series of linked articles is called a thread. See also Usenet.

backbone The high-speed part of the Internet's physical infrastructure. It comprises high-speed cable and satellite data links that can handle vast quantities of data and span thousands of miles.

bandwidth A term used to describe the information-carrying capacity of a network or the pipelines that connect networks. The bigger the bandwidth, the faster your Internet connection runs.

banner An advert that appears on a web page, usually in the form of a wide, thin box at the top of the page. These are often used on travel websites to bring news of special flight offers to your attention.

bookmark A generic term for a marker reference to a website address saved by your browser software. Microsoft Internet Explorer refers to them as favorites.

Boolean system A system of logical expressions developed more than 100 years ago by the mathematician George Boole and now used to help define searches on the Internet. See page 45.

browser The software used to access websites. Microsoft's Internet Explorer and Netscape's Navigator are the two most popular examples.

cache A directory used by your browser software to store on your hard drive information, text and graphics you glean. This stored information can speed up later visits to those websites, because the browser can take a large proportion of content from the cache instead of downloading it from the website.

client Any piece of software that fetches information from the Internet, an example being your web browser. See also the entry for server.

cookie A small file sent by a web server to store on your PC, which can later be read back by the server. This means it can tell when you visit again, and can remember specific information about you that can be used automatically next time you connect to the site.

crawler See entry for spider.

cyber café Also sometimes known as an Internet café, any establishment that offers Internet access on a pay-as-you-use basis – together with cakes and coffee.

cyberspace A now rather overused name for the virtual world of information that the Internet creates.

dial-up The usual method of connecting to the Internet via an Internet Service Provider and telephone connection.

digital certificate A form of electronic identity card, programmed into many e-commerce websites. When you connect to make a payment for services or goods, the digital certificate confirms to your browser that the website you are connecting to belongs to the company in question, helping to protect you against fraud. See also SSL.

domain The distinctive name given to a server attached to the Internet. For example, in **http://www.virgin-books.com**, the domain part of the address is virgin-books.com.

downloading The process of transferring information (such as an email message or the images and text that make up a web page) from the Internet on to your computer. The reverse process, sending information from your PC through the Internet to another computer, is known as uploading.

DNS (Domain Name System) The method by which the complex numerical addresses used by Internet computers are converted into relatively easy-to-remember textual URLs, and vice versa.

e-commerce Buying and selling goods or services across the Internet.

executable Any computer file that you have to 'run' in order for it to work, a good example being your browser.

FAQ (Frequently Asked Questions) Common queries and their answers. Many travel websites have a FAQ page that will familiarise you with how the site and the company operate. Read it.

flaming Blowing your top, losing your temper or taking someone down a peg or two online. People often get 'flamed' in newsgroups for breaching the rules of etiquette. See also netiquette.

frames Separate windows displayed in your browser by a website. A common example is a navigation bar that stays the same while the content changes in the main window.

GIF (Graphics Interchange Format) A type of image file used on websites. See also the entry for JPEG.

hierarchy The way newsgroups are grouped together and categorised. There are eight main hierarchies: alt. (alternative); comp. (computing); misc. (miscellaneous); news. (news); rec. (recreation); sci. (science); soc. (society) and talk. (discussion). Within each group there can be hundreds of specific newsgroups.

hits The number of matching references found by a search engine, or the number of visitors to any website.

home page The first, or front, page of any website – the one you normally see when you connect to the site.

HTML (HyperText Markup Language) The computer code used to build websites. It is a system of commands that tells your browser what to display on screen.

http (HyperText Transfer Protocol) The complex set of rules and instructions used to send information around the Internet.

hyperlink (or link) Components of a web page that enable users to access different pieces of information by using a mouse click. A hyperlink may jump to another section of the same page, or to a different page or website altogether.

IE See Internet Explorer.

image map Often seen on travel websites, any picture that has specific areas designed to act as site navigation links. A good example would be the one sometimes used by hotel directories: a map of the world that lets you click on a country, and then takes you to that part of the hotel directory.

Internet Explorer The popular web browser developed by Microsoft. It is often called by its acronym of IE – usually followed by the version number to give IE4 or IE5.

IRC (Internet Relay Chat) The technology that enables people to talk online by exchanging text messages.

ISP (Internet Service Provider) A company that acts as the link between your computer and the Internet.

Java A programming language used widely on the web. It is often used to create small applications known as 'applets', such as a news ticker, to enhance the page.

JPEG (Joint Photographic Experts Group) A way of compressing image files without serious loss of detail. Because they are quick to download, they are very popular with website designers.

Kbps (kilobits per second) The rate at which information is sent down a computer connection. The current standard for a modem is 56Kbps.

keyword term Or set of terms used to categorise web pages – or to describe what you are looking for when using a search engine. See also metadata.

leased line A fast, 'always on' link between an organisation and an ISP. Mostly used by businesses because of the high installation and operating costs.

lurker Someone who reads but doesn't write to an online discussion forum such as Usenet or IRC. While some might tell you otherwise, there is nothing wrong with being a lurker.

mailbox The directory on your computer's hard drive where your email messages are stored when you collect them from your ISP. See mail server.

mail server The computer at your ISP where all your incoming email gets delivered and stored until you collect it, like an electronic pigeon-hole.

metadata Information about information, used by websites to help search engines to index them effectively. Every well-designed web page contains metadata in the form of keywords that describe its content. This cannot be seen by the web browser.

modem Hardware used by that most home PC owners to connect a computer to the Internet via their telephone line. Modems convert digital computer information into sounds and back again.

MPEG (Motion Picture Experts Group) An organisation that developed a format for high-quality video for the PC – and thence, any video produced in this format.

name server A computer that matches the URL typed into a browser or contained in a hyperlink to the numerical address used by the Internet to identify the other server. See also DNS.

netiquette A set of informal guidelines for acceptable behaviour while online. This mainly applies to the use of email and newsgroups. An excellent guide to netiquette can be found at **http://www.fau.edu/netiquette**.

network Any collection of interconnected computers that are capable of exchanging information with each other. Local Area Networks (LANs) consist of a relatively small number of computers within a single building or organisation. The Internet, on the other hand, is the world's largest network – with millions of computers attached to it.

newbie A derogative slang expression for someone who is new to the Internet.

newsgroup A discussion group on a specific subject. There are 30,000 or so separate newsgroups to choose from. See page 10.

newsreader The software program used to access Usenet newsgroups.

password Combination of letters and/or numbers that, in combination with a username, identifies you to an ISP or a web-based service. If asked to make up a password, don't use real words that others may guess such as pet names or swearwords. Don't write it down and don't tell anyone else what it is.

plug-in Software application that works with your browser to add features – like the ability to hear music.

portal Web gateway that acts as a central focal point for web access. These are often organised in directory style, offering links to popular websites, in-house editorial content and added value services such as free email.

RealPlayer Music and video player sometimes used by travel websites to add multimedia presentations to the page. You can download a player at **http://www.real.com**.

router Server that passes information to other routers on the Internet to ensure data reaches its destination. There are hundreds of thousands of routers on the Internet.

search engine Website that helps you to find other websites. See page 39.

secure server Internet-connected computer that uses complex codes to encrypt your credit card details, thus preventing anyone from using them fraudulently. See also SSL.

server Any computer connected to the Internet that holds information. A web server, for example, holds the information that make up websites and will send that data to web browser clients on request.

smiley Small faces, created using keyboard characters, which you view sideways. They are used to help show emotions in email and online chat. Sometimes called emoticons.

spam The email equivalent of junk mail – such as unsolicited emails offering to make you money or sell you something.

spider Software program that crawls around the web looking for new pages to index for a search engine database. Most of the large search engines use a spider of some sort to collect and update information.

SSL (Secure Sockets Layer) Technology used by secure servers to ensure you are communicating securely with the website concerned. SSL offers the necessary security when making credit card payments online.

thread In the context of newsgroups a particular strand of conversation within any given discussion. Most newsreaders will automatically 'thread' messages into a conversational order for ease of reading.

thumbnail Small postage-stamp-sized representations of a larger image, used to speed up the loading of a web page. Many travel sites feature destination photos as thumbnails. Click on the small image to see the full-sized one.

uploading See downloading.

URL (Uniform Resource Locator) Standard address format for accessing Internet services, most commonly associated with website addresses.

Usenet The Internet's global noticeboard consisting of more than 30,000 individual areas each covering a specific subject matter. See also newsgroup.

VRML (Virtual Reality Modelling Language) Little-used technology that can be used to create 3D effects on a website.

web space The part of a server's hard disk where web pages reside. If your ISP says you have 10Mb web space, this means they have allocated you 10Mb of space on a web server's hard drive.

wizard An application that helps to automate an online task for the user. Examples in the travel field include hotel- and flight-finding services.

WWW The most commonly used abbreviated form of World Wide Web.

//INDEX

//THE FRESHEST SITES, THE SMARTEST TIPS, THE BEST ADVICE

Also published in the Virgin Internet series...

The Virgin Guide to the Internet by Simon Collin
The advice you need to plug in, log on and get going...

The Virgin Family Internet Guide by Simon Collin
The only book that lets your family get the best out of the Internet
– and lock out the worst.

The Virgin Internet Shopping Guide by Simon Collin
You can now buy almost anything on the Internet, and this book
shows you how.

Forthcoming titles:

The Virgin Internet Money Guide
Use your modem to make the most of your money.

The Virgin Internet Music Guide
The web is alive – with the sound of music.

For more information, ask your friendly local bookseller – or check
out our website: **http://www.virgin-books.com**